What the Experts

MW00620230

"It is an encyclopedia of practic
use. The text is well-organized
section as needed. I very much
recommended reading list for pa

-Sam Goldstein, PhD,
Salt Lake City, Utah

Sam Goldstein is a Child Psychologist at the Neurology Learning & Behavior Center in
Salt Lake City, Utah. He is the author of *Managing Attention Disorders in Children and
Hyperactivity: Why Won't My Child Pay Attention?*

● ●

"This book is a must read for any teacher, parent, or person who suspects they
have ADD or they have a child with ADD. You can't teach today without
encountering this challenge. I grew up ADD before this was a known pattern.
I was also hyperactive and dyslexic. What a great advantage it would have
been to have had this life-changing information. These tips can improve self-
management and parenting even without the challenges of ADD. Prepare to
enjoy growing."

-Dr Ann McGee-Cooper
Dallas, TX

Dr. Ann McGee-Cooper conducts conferences across the nation on time management and
is the author of several books, including *Time Management for Unmanageable People*.

● ●

"A clever, comprehensive, thoughtful book, overflowing with practical solutions
for hundreds of difficult situations at home and school. Must reading for any concerned parent, teacher, or ADDult."

-John Taylor, Ph.D.
Salem, Oregon

John Taylor is the author of *Helping Your Hyperactive ADD Child.*

● ●

"This is a real pearl. As the father of an ADD child and a physician who has
treated many children with ADD, I can appreciate the practical suggestions. I
like your down to earth, tried and tested suggestions based on experience and
not theory. This is a welcomed, easy to use, guide."

-Frank E. Crumley, M.D.
Dallas, Texas

Dr. Frank Crumley is a psychiatrist and works with both adults and children.

● ●

"Reading ADD Quick Tips...I saw myself described in such detail it was almost
embarrassing. Several times, I laughed out loud. Mainly I learned many techniques...that I will apply to my own time management and counseling of my
ADD patients. This book should be a resource for every teacher and every ADD
family."

-Wayne Jones, M.D.
Richardson, Texas

Dr. Wayne Jones is a psychiatrist and works with both adults and children.

Other books by Carla Crutsinger

Teenage Connection: *A Tool for Effective Teenage Communication*
Thinking Smarter: *Skills for Academic Success*
Creative Memory: *An Alternative to Rote Learning*

Other books by Carla Crutsinger and Debra Moore

Most Wanted Words: *A New Approach to Spelling, Writing, and Thinking*

Brainworks, Inc.
1918 Walnut Plaza
Carrollton, TX 75006-5856
(972) 416-9410

ADD QUICK TIPS

Practical Ways to Manage Attention Deficit Disorder Successfully

Carla Crutsinger
Debra Moore

BRAINWORKS®

Brainworks®
1918 Walnut Plaza
Carrollton, TX 75006-5856
(972) 416-9410

Dedication

Sam Crutsinger

For Debra's "support group" of friends:
John & Kay
Sarah ("The Pie")
"Big Bad" John
John, Barbara & Hunter
Little Nancy
"Big Debbie" & Halley
Tom, Melinda, Ian, and Phyllis
Joy, Danny & Boomer-Rang

"Love is patient, love is kind. It does not envy, it does not boast, it is not proud. It is not rude, it is not self-seeking, it is not easily angered, it keeps no record of wrongs. Love does not delight in evil but rejoices with the truth. It always protects, always trusts, always hopes, always perseveres."
-1 Corinthians 13: 4-7.
New International Version

A Few Words for the ADD Student

by Debra Moore

Although this book is written about you, the ADD student, most of what's said in these pages is directed at parents, teachers, tutors, counselors, and ADD coaches. The book's aim is to give the adults around you some hints which would, in the long run, make your life easier.

We also hope reading about these tips will help adults reach a better understanding about how we ADDers "tick." One of the best parts about my job at Brainworks is I get to connect with fellow members of my "tribe" on a daily basis.

I know we are a difficult group to categorize and analyze. By nature, we are unpredictable, unorthodox, and unregulated; one minute we are exuberant and dramatically passionate, and sixty seconds later, we may lapse into passive dreaminess. Our tendency to operate on "impulse power" can be exciting or aggravating, depending on the circumstances. (My friends may get annoyed at me when I'm impulsively changing dinner plans, but they are far more tolerant of my impulsivity when I'm shopping for their birthday presents!)

Despite the fact that my undiagnosed ADD complicated the first 38 years of my life, I can honestly say, "I wouldn't want to be any other way." ADD has blessed me with a number of positive qualities, including an active imagination, a spontaneous sense of humor, and a heightened sense of compassion.

However, I'd be lying if I didn't also acknowledge the negative impact of ADD; I've lost friends, changed jobs, and felt like a failure because I wasn't reaching my "potential." Being diagnosed was an important first step, but the next step was up to me. I had to learn to manage my ADD negatives. To do this, I had to "let go" of a great deal of guilt and bad feelings from my past. I said, "Ok, from now on, you have a responsibility to identify your ADD problems and figure out a way around them."

It hasn't always been an easy battle, but I have made a number of positive changes in my life. I hope this book helps you see some positive changes as well. To help you out, here are some special "tips" just for you!

1. Find a "quiet place" for yourself somewhere, a place where you can sit by yourself and spend time thinking for and about YOU. Dream about the great stuff you plan to do; it's an excellent way to develop your "anticipation skills," and dreams have an uncanny way of turning into goals.

2. Be kind to yourself. Don't call yourself, "stupid" when you experience a setback. Don't say anything to yourself that you wouldn't say to your best friend under the same circumstances.

Work consciously to say "good things" to yourself also. Before you go to sleep each night, think about one success you had that day, or make a list of "why people like me."

3. Work on "delaying reactions" to what people say to you. Most of the conflicts I've known happened because I tended to "leap to the defensive" when I misunderstood people. Now I ask, "What did you mean by that?" before I react, and this little question has headed off a lot of arguments!

4. Identify your special talents and pursue them. Many ADDers possess artistic gifts, such as drawing, dancing, or playing a musical instrument. Others are terrific mechanics, cooks, campers, or computer "hackers." Whatever it is that you do best, work at becoming better at it. Your talent may lead to a successful career !

5. Learn as much as you can about ADD. The more you know about the nature of the condition, the better able you are to control the negatives and exploit the positives.

6. Cultivate friendships with non-ADDers. I realize now how important it has been to have non-ADD folks in my life, and generally, such "combinations of opposites"are worthwhile for both sides.

Good luck!

A Few Words...
For the Parents of ADD
Students
    by Carla Crutsinger

As I thumb through these pages, one thought that pops into my mind is, "Boy, I sure wish I'd had a book like this when my son was still in school!" It's amazing for me to consider the advances made in understanding and treating ADD in the twenty-two years since my son Sam was in the first grade.

Whenever I recall his struggles, I remember the pain he suffered; as a parent, I saw his zest for life and his joy for learning deteriorate a little bit each day. Even in elementary school, he experienced the confusion and frustration typical to many ADD students; he was intelligent enough to do his work, but he couldn't manage to finish assignments on time, to remember to study for tests, or to keep track of his textbooks. Long-term projects were simply out of the question!

He seemed to be constantly in the academic "frying pan," and his grades went up and down like a yo-yo. In one six weeks, he would fail a subject, but on his next report card, he'd make an A in that class but fail another subject! The only consistent factor was inconsistency.

As a parent, I grew very tired of having to monitor his efforts on assignments, yet I was torn between allowing him to fail as a "lesson learned" consequence and watch his self-esteem crumble—or continuing to play the role of his "Homework Cop." Over time, the quality of our relationship began to change as a result of my "nagging" him to stay on task, and I realized, "For the rest of his life, my son will remember his childhood as a time of torture." I certainly didn't want that!

His teachers assumed he was "lazy" and "didn't care." However, some subjects did interest him, and in those classes he made "A's." In other classes, he'd lose his attention five minutes after he walked through the door.

In a moment of desperation, I made a bargain with God, praying "If you get us through this crisis and help me discover what is happening to Sam, I will devote my life to helping others with similar problems."

It takes a long time for some prayers to be answered, but eight years later, we finally discovered that Sam was dealing with ADD and other learning complications. Treating his ADD gave him new options. This gifted young man went from narrowly managing to graduate from high school to earning a college degree in four years, and in the last year, he made the Dean's List! He majored in radio, television and film production and eventually entered the field of film and video productions; in the course of his career, he won an "Emmy" for his work on a television documentary. Currently, he is director of corporate technology of a national advertising agency, and he has worked as an audio engineer for television commercials and as a computer and graphics consultant for many businesses—including his mother's company!

Sam's triumph mirrors the achievements we have seen over and over in our clients' lives for the last 16 years. As we move into the 21st century, I see a new horizon of opportunities for ADDers, and I am especially pleased at how well schools are beginning to train teachers to adapt instructive strategies to fit various learning styles. I also find hope in the fact that research has added so much information to the body of knowledge about ADD, and doctors are responding to this knowledge. As scientific investigation continues, more effective treatments and management therapies will be available for ADDers. ADD "success stories" will continue to grow in number thanks to these advances.

God answered my prayer, and I hope this book helps you and your child find the path to a better and brighter future .

Acknowledgments

Without the contributions of several key individuals, this project would never have reached completion. Katy McDaniel provided valuable insights and information regarding the needs and abilities of primary grade ADD students; her expertise in elementary education issues and foundational learning skills gave us crucial background information for the tips aimed at "younger ADDers." She also assisted us by proofreading the book and helping compile the index and appendix sections.

Jan Bourg is our "math specialist" at Brainworks, and she offered many excellent suggestions for dealing with ADD math issues. In addition, she and her son Andrew served as "models" for our photographs on handwriting skills.

Assembling the text and graphics for this book was a formidable challenge, and we were fortunate to have had the keyboarding talents of Debbie Heffler and Tammy Sumner available for the project. Despite the computer headaches and hassles, they managed to stay "on task" and get the job done. We are grateful for their dedication and their energy.

Finally, we would like to thank the ADD clients who come to our facility for help. Without their "real life" problems, we wouldn't have been challenged to develop "real life" solutions.

Table of Contents

		Page
INTRODUCTION		5

Part One
ADD QUICK TIPS FOR TEENS/ADULTS

Organization Options. 19

Time Tips 45

Study Strategies 83

Personal Pointers. 133

Part Two
QUICK TIPS FOR YOUNGER ADDERS

Time and Space. 193

Study Strategies. 219

Personal Pointers. 269

Appendix 311
Index 329

INTRODUCTION

 The Creation of Brainworks

 Answers for ADD Questions

 Using this Book

 A Disorder of Desperation

 Management = Success

 Quick Tip Guidelines

INTRODUCTION

The Creation of Brainworks

In 1997, the Brainworks Educational Center celebrated its 16th year of providing innovative programs for individuals who desire to improve their thinking skills. The center was founded by a professional educator, Carla Crutsinger, in response to her search for a facility which could help her gifted son achieve academic and personal success, an achievement complicated by his struggles with Attention Deficit Disorder (ADD). Eventually, Carla reached the conclusion that there was no single place which offered the diverse range of services she sought as well as the individual focus and intellectual stimulation her son required. It was clear, however, that there was a need for such an institution, and in 1981, Brainworks was created to fill that need.

Since then, hundreds of people from the ages of 5 to 75 have come to Brainworks for assessment and remediation of a wide variety of learning problems. Our staff works one-on-one with children and adolescents during regular "after school" sessions; adult tutorials are set up by appointment. Each person's unique combination of strengths and deficiencies presents our instructors with the challenge of designing plans to help the client reach the academic, professional, and personal goals which translate into a successful life.

Answers for ADD Questions

From the beginning, Brainworks has been an ideal resource for people who needed help managing their negative ADD symptoms. While the center does not exclusively focus on ADD issues, it is true that ADDers account for the majority of our clients at any given time. In particular, we have worked with "school age" ADDers who, at some phase of the educational process, have "crashed" into an academic wall of overwhelming proportions. For some ADDers, this crash occurs in the primary grades. For others, it may come in middle or high school, and for some it happens in college, graduate school, or during training in medical or law school. But no matter what the age, the issues faced by these diverse individuals follow strikingly similar patterns: problems with organization, time, and study skills compounded by difficulties with more personal areas, such as health, motivation, and behavior.

As we worked with ADD clients, we learned a great deal about how ADDers can best cope with the demands of this modern world. These clients gave us an opportunity to discover "what works" for them, and as they resolved their situations, they provided us with the strategies and insights which form the substance of **ADD Quick Tips.**

Using This Book

When the staff of Brainworks began to assemble the information contained in this book, we decided to focus on making it as "user friendly" as possible. First of all, the format was set up for quick reference purposes by dividing the information into four broad topic sections, alliteratively designated as Organization Options, Time Tips, Study Strategies, and Personal Pointers. Within each of these sections, a group of suggestions (or "tips") are offered in response to questions we have heard repeatedly from parents, teachers, and ADD students. In addition, we have included a separate category of tips which address the special needs of ADD children between the ages of 5 to 12. This section is called Quick Tips for Younger ADDers.

We also decided early on to present practical, realistic strategies in specific language and to avoid "theoretical" discussions and/or general descriptions of ADD behavior. If the reader of this book has ADD, he or she is probably quite familiar with the disorder's definition and diagnostic criteria from a lifetime of experience, and the same familiarity holds true for those readers who have ADDers in the family or the classroom.

Moreover, we realized there are currently a number of excellent books already on the market which offer background information about the condition by examining the possible causes of ADD, delineating the symptoms, or describing case studies of various individuals with ADD. Our goal was to create a book specifically designed to provide strategies for resolving the problems of ADD students. This book primarily offers concrete methods to resolve real-life issues for ADDers; when an explanation seemed necessary in order to understand how a tip works, we have tried to keep these comments as concise as possible. Most importantly, this book is based on experience, not theories; every tip has been "tried and tested" by our clients.

A Disorder of Desperation

By the time ADD students arrive at our door, they are usually in desperate straits. Their inability to cope with the myriad details of their lives have caused them to fail one or more classes, and as their grades fall, their self-esteem also tumbles. Ironically, many of our ADD clients are also highly intelligent, gifted individuals; however, the disorder prevents them from achieving according to their capabilities, a situation which further fuels their frustrations.

Because so much emphasis has been placed on their deficiencies, ADDers tend to identify themselves by what they cannot do instead of what they can do. Yet, as Dr. Edward Hallowell (and many other ADD researchers) have pointed out, there may be as many advantages connected to ADD as there are problems. These "positive points" include creativity, flexibility, intuition, risk-taking, and independent thinking.

Unfortunately for the ADDer, school systems tend to stress the very traits which are not part of the ADD make-up, such as conformity, obedience, attentiveness, and organization. It's little wonder many ADDers are diagnosed as a result of their behavior in classrooms, for in that setting the ADD student is truly a "square peg in a round hole."

Management = Success

At Brainworks, we address ADD problems from several directions. First of all, we teach the clients strategies for managing the negative ADD characteristics which interfere with their ability to achieve academically. As they begin to have more positive classroom experiences, their self-confidence grows, and they become "empowered students." Secondly, we increase their self awareness, encouraging them to analyze the ADD emotional reactions and behaviors which can negatively affect their self-image and their relationships with others. The "typical" ADD behavior pattern involves extreme shifts in mood and perspective, resulting in a great deal of tension within and around the ADDer. By documenting these behavior patterns, we help ADDers learn to anticipate and control their reactions. Finally, we encourage them to be more aware of their strengths, and we train them in ways to use those strengths to overcome their present deficiencies.

The underlying premise for our program and for these tips is: **"ADD problems need ADD solutions."** In other words, we should not expect ADDers to respond positively to strategies which work with non-ADD students. Instead, we need "ADD friendly" methods which incorporate their special set of characteristics. It is our firm belief that ADDers can reach the "peak of success" although they may have to travel non-traditional paths to get there.

Quick Tips Guidelines

 **Do Not Attempt A Tip Without Reviewing This Section!**

Parents, teachers, and ADD students should keep these points in mind before beginning to work on a tip:

1. The ADD student must acknowledge and understand the need to work on the tip. Establishing that need may require tracking and documenting the problem situation.

2. The ADD student must be an active participant in choosing and using the tip. If the tip is "forced" on the student, it will not be effective. Remember: The point of learning a problem–solving skill is to develop independence, something which is not likely to occur under duress.

3. Work on no more than one or two tips at a time and set goals within reasonable time frames. Do not commit to trial periods longer than two weeks; for younger ADD students, one week experiments are more realistic. Establish a "time

table" to measure mastery. For example, if the student successfully maintains his assignment calendar and has no zeros in any class for 12 weeks, he can suspend having teachers sign his folder or having parents check his homework for six weeks. However, be sure to build in a "back up" plan for renewing the tip if the problem recurs.

4. Commit to the tip in writing. Have the student write (or type) the goal and the steps to be followed, including the time frame mentioned above. The student and parents should "sign off" on the plan to signify the commitment.

5. Expect the need to "fine tune" the strategies after the first trial period. The student, family members, and possibly the teachers should review the goal and evaluate the progress. Discuss what changes (if any) need to be made and create a list of options for the future.

Most importantly, parents, teachers, family members, friends, and ADDers themselves must be aware that **no tip, plan, or strategy is a "permanent fix" for any ADD problem.** The shifting nature of the condition dictates that no management technique works forever; inevitably, old strategies will need to be adjusted and new tactics developed to address the student's needs. This situation often frustrates those who work with ADDers, for as soon as a problem seems "under control" and everyone starts to relax, then suddenly the same problem pops back up again, perhaps in an even worse form!

The best way to avoid discouragement about these lapses is to recognize the implications of the term "managed." It doesn't mean ADD can be "cured" or "solved." It means **ADD can be controlled,** much in the manner that a border collie controls a herd of sheep; the job requires vigilance, flexible responses, and perseverance.

6. Reward progress with praise IMMEDIATELY and FREQUENTLY. Analyze any setbacks in detail, making sure the focus is on the problem, not the student. ("What can you do to raise this grade in math to a C?" instead of "How could anyone not understand long division?")

7. Parents and teachers should try the tips themselves. If the parent is also an ADDer (and according to genetics, it's a distinct possibility), he or she might learn some new techniques which could make life easier. On the other hand, if the adults involved do not have ADD, they should practice using the tips in order to gain a better appreciation for what the ADD student is trying to accomplish.

8. Adults should not set higher expectations for the child than they do for themselves. Well-meaning parents sometimes pressure their children about the very areas in which the parents themselves feel insecure. The basis of this very natural and instinctive concern can be summed up as "I don't want my kid to go through what I've gone through." However, from the child's perspective, the parental attitude may seem hypocritical, and the student's response may be negative as a result. "Why do they get mad at me for being tardy to class when they're never on time to pick me up from school?" In other words, "If you can't walk on water, don't expect your child to!" Instead, parents should attempt to model the skills which they want the child to develop.

Part One

ADD Quick Tips
for
Teenagers/Adults

Organization Options

INTRODUCTION

AT HOME

 How Can An ADD Student Get Organized At Home?

 How Can An ADD Student Get More Organized With Homework?

 What Can Work As Reminders For ADD Students?

 How Did ADD Students Function Before The Invention Of The Post-it® Notes?

AT SCHOOL

 How Can The ADD Student Be More Organized At School?

 Why Do ADD Students Always Carry Overloaded Backpacks?

 What Organizer Supplies Work Best For ADD Students?

INTRODUCTION

Organization Options

Certainly, disorganization is one of the most noticeable traits connected with Attention Deficit Disorder. For non-ADDers it may be one of the most annoying characteristics with which to live. If we look at the physical world of the ADD student (the desk snowed under by piles, the book bag overflowing with papers, the bedroom cluttered with pictures and "stuff"), the word "chaos" may come to mind. Some people may even view this hectic environment as an indicator of the "scatter-brained" mentality of those with ADD.

However, the person with ADD has a different perspective of this issue. ADDers are visual thinkers; to them, the words "tidy and organized" may be synonymous with "sterile and boring." What some call "clutter" serves as both a stimulus and a comfort to ADDers. Many of them simply cannot function in an empty room with barren walls, a characteristic which will probably not change throughout their lifetimes despite threats, coaxing, or bribes.

In addition, ADDers use spatial and visual cues for recall. In other words, they locate something by remembering what the item looks like and where the item is placed in relation to other

**out of sight–
out of mind**

objects. Ask the ADD student to find his notebook, and a picture flashes in his mind (like a close-up snapshot) of the last place the notebook was **seen**. Once an object is removed from sight (as in a desk drawer), the item is "lost" because it is removed from the visual frame of reference. For the ADDer, "out of sight" is truly "out of mind."

This situation explains why traditional "organizers"often don't work for people with ADD. Putting papers in file folders is useless because all manila folders look alike; moreover, putting the folders in the cabinet is about as helpful as putting them in the trash can.

Instead, ADDers tend to use "piles" to store paperwork in plain sight, a technique which can get out of control as time passes and as school assignments multiply. Fortunately, there are a number of strategies which can assist visual organizers at home and at school.

However, it important to keep in mind that a person's organizational method is measured by **how it works, not how it looks.** We know an ADD adult whose home, desk, and office often look like a random collection of jumbled piles, yet this same person can usually find a specific item or memo instantly. The system may not be "pretty" to the non-ADD eye, but it is functional.

If the ADD student can find what she is looking for in less than two minutes, the system works; if not, the ADDer needs to try some of the coping tips presented in the following pages. And if parents or non-ADDers find looking at so much "clutter and stuff" in the ADD student's room unbearable, they should consider closing the door. Some battles just aren't worth the energy!

**Pick and choose
your battles.**

How Can An ADD Student Get Organized At Home?

1. Use desk tops, counters and open shelves to store piles of "in progress" materials. Designate one corner of the desk for English papers, another corner for science work, the center for history assignments, and so forth.
(Shelves or bookcases with glass covers can be great for storing the seemingly endless bits of minutia ADDers attract so effortlessly on a daily basis.)

Tack reminders to the bulletin board.

2. Tack papers on large cork bulletin boards to keep them in view with less clutter. (For younger children, use a metal bulletin board with magnets instead of tacks.)

3. Adapt a large "walk-in" closet to hold a desk or counters and make it the student's office area. This "mini-office" gives the student what is often called a "distraction free" zone (see Study Strategies Chapter), and it permits the student to "tidy up" by simply shutting the closet door.

4. Remove the mattress from the bottom half of a bunk bed or a trundle bed to create space for materials. Use a quilt or blanket as a "tidy up" cover.

5. Designate a "clutter spot" in the ADD student's room. It can be a drawer (which can be closed) or a corner (which can be covered, screened or blocked by furniture). This area becomes the "catch-all" zone for items which can-not be easily sorted or which need to be handy on a daily basis.

Drawers can store miscellaneous ADD "stuff."

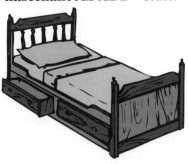

How Can ADD Students Get More Organized With Homework?

The struggle to recall, finish, and return homework assignments is one of the toughest challenges faced by ADD students, but the situation is not an impossible one.

1. Assignment Sheets: Many schools (even in primary grades) now require students to keep assignment sheets for scheduling homework or test dates. As well-intentioned as these sheets may be, ADDers often have problems using them. First of all, the sheet gets mixed in with other papers and is lost. Secondly, the design of these sheets (which often resemble calendar grids) are not "ADD friendly" since one black and white box looks pretty much like another to the ADD eye.

Some tips can help the assignment sheet work as it should. First, try photocopying assignment sheets on brightly colored paper or put a color "tab" on the edge, so the student can find the sheet more easily. Then, set up a "permanent spot" for the sheet in a place clearly visible to the students. (Some notebooks have transparent plastic covers with zip-lock edges; the inside of this cover is a great location.) Class assignments can be written in colors coded to each class (blue for history, red for math, etc.)

One of the best ways to make assignment sheets more ADD friendly is to let the student experiment with designing her own sheet. This strategy allows the student to use the ADD gift of creativity and lowers the student's resistance to a structure which is self-generated rather than imposed by an authority.

2. Another basic problem regarding assignment sheets is getting the student into the routine of writing the assignments for each subject every day. In order to develop the habit, for **at least** six weeks, each teacher should check the student's assignment sheet at the end of class and initial the block if the

WRITE IT DOWN

Written down assignments are rarely forgotten.

assignment is written correctly. Many teachers have homework assignments posted in clear view throughout the class period and follow a standard routine for picking up and returning papers. These techniques are helpful for all students, but they are especially helpful for ADD students.

3. If there is no homework assignment, the student should write "no homework" or "NHW" in the block and have that initialed as well. **This step is very important!** It gets the student in the routine of writing in every block, and it verifies that there is no homework–not that the student just forgot to write it down.

Teacher initials every assignment block, even the NHW.

4. Establish a single "pocket" folder for all the homework done by the ADD student. Students who try to keep English homework in one section, history in another, etc., will end up

spending more time searching for their homework than they spent doing their homework. (Students should set up one pocket for work to be handed in and another pocket for returned papers.)

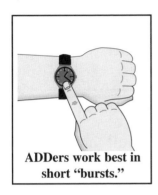

ADDers work best in short "bursts."

5. ADD students often work best in short "bursts," and if they have several homework assignments to do, they may be able to spend only about 15-20 minutes at a time on one task before becoming bored. By switching back and forth between tasks, they may actually do a better job in less time.

The problem comes if the student forgets to return and complete an assignment, particularly if he "puts away" a paper before it is finished. Since ADDers operate visually, homework put inside a book or notebook is likely to be forgotten.

Keep all unfinished papers in sight. If the study area does need to be cleared, the student can put the incomplete paper half-way in the book, with the paper's edge sticking out to signal "unfinished."

6. Locate a peer "study buddy" who can help make sure all homework assignments are recorded. This study buddy should sit near the ADD student, and they should exchange home phone numbers in case there is a question about an assignment.

What Can Work As "Reminders" For An ADD Student?

Since the ADD mind races full throttle most of the time, many necessary details of life get lost on a regular basis. The ADDer says, "Oh, I'll remember to take my library books back," but somehow the mental note disappears in the rush of a thousand other thoughts, and before the student realizes it, a library fine starts to grow. Parents should also be aware that excessive verbal reminders (i.e. "nagging") suffer the same fate as this mental note!

The best reminders for ADD students are based on visual, tactile, or auditory cues. Note: Reminders work best with planned "back-ups." **Always** have at least two reminders set up to remember really important information.

Use a variety of reminders.

1. Alarm clocks are for more than waking up! Use an alarm clock throughout the day to remember to make phone calls, do chores, start homework, take medication, etc. Put a note for the student on the alarm "off switch" of the clock if a more detailed reminder is necessary. (Kitchen clocks/timers are also good for signaling "time to do something.")

2. The old-fashioned "tie a string around your finger" technique still works. Other variations include: putting a marble in the student's pocket or tying a knotted handkerchief on purse or book bag straps. (Make sure tactile reminders cause no discomfort to sometimes "skin sensitive" ADDers.)

Use the answering machine as a personal reminder.

3. If a student away from home needs to recall information when she returns, the ADDer should call and leave a message to herself on the home answering machine.

4. If a student has to make a quick note to himself, he can write a word or an abbreviation on his hand. Fortunately, nearly all pens and markers contain washable ink, but ADDers should be careful

not to use permanent markers for this tip! (Many ADD adults have learned to use this coping technique on their own. As one of them put it, "I might lose a paper note or forget to look at it. It's hard to lose or ignore my left hand!")

5. The ADDer can ask a non-ADD friend or family member to call at a certain time for wake-up calls or as a "back-up" reminder about important appointments. (This service must be **requested** by the ADDer in order to remove it from the category of "nagging." For the same reason, these reminders work best if they come from people outside the family circle.)

6. Place a "dry erase" memo board directly across from the student's bed for writing reminders for the next morning. (Some families keep one board for the student and another for family reminders.)

How Did Students Function Before The Invention of Post-it® Notes?

We don't know how ADDers functioned before the invention of Post-it® notes, but these handy and colorful pads help our ADD clients of all ages cope with the details of modern life. The notes serve not only as reminders, but also as motivators and "thought catchers."

Remember-
Return
library books
today!

The most crucial issue our clients face with using the note pads involves **placement**. Here are some tips to get the maximum benefit from Post-it® note reminders.

1. Have blank pads available in many spots, not just in a desk drawer. Good spots include: in the car, in the kitchen, near a favorite chair, inside a wallet or calendar/planner, next to the bed, and even in the bathroom.

2. Reminder notes should be placed in appropriate spots. For example, a note to remind the ADDer to take out the garbage before leaving the house should be put at eye level on the exit door. Or, a note regarding items which should be in the car before leaving the driveway could be put on the dashboard.

Some good places to leave notes include: television or computer screens, shoes which will be worn the next day, bathroom mirrors, stereos, etc. Learn the ADDer's best spots. The mother of one of our clients knew her son drank a glass of juice after school. She tried leaving notes on the refrigerator door, but she got better results from putting the notes **inside** the refrigerator on the juice bottle!

Post-it® notes can also provide motivation (See Personal Pointers Chapter).

Pick up
Josh at
Basketball
4:30 pm

How Can An ADD Student Be More Organized At School?

1. Use lockers to sort books, not just store them. If the ADD student has a locker with a shelf, he can use the shelf to help him sort his books into "homework tonight" and "no homework tonight" divisions. (Books on top go home; books on the bottom stay at school.) **This sorting process should occur as soon as possible after each class.** If the student waits till the end of the day, he will be trying to remember the assignments for several classes while rushing to exit–a situation which is not conducive to recalling details.

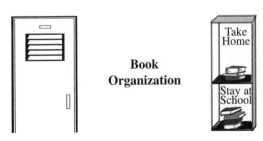

Book Organization

If the student's locker has no shelf, locker inserts are available at organizer stores. If lockers are not used at the student's school, use the same "sorting" strategy with the student's desk (books on the left are for homework, and books on the right are not).

2. Some ADD students have problems correctly writing standard format headings on their papers (name, subject, class, date, etc.), particularly on in-class assignments. In the hustle to get the paper handed in, having the proper heading is one of those details which the ADDer may miss; however, some teachers may deduct points from papers which don't follow the format.

During quiet times at home, the student should go ahead and write the proper headings (except for the date) on blank sheets of paper. When it's time for an in-class assignment, the student uses his prepared sheets; all he has to do is fill in the date.

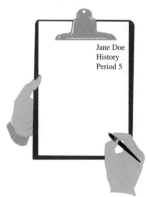

Why Do ADD Students Always Carry Overloaded Backpacks?

Backpacks and book bags can be helpful tools for ADD students. On the other hand, they can become crowded "Bermuda Triangles" into which papers and supplies disappear without a trace. This situation occurs because the bag is being used for **storage instead of transportation.**

Use backpacks for transportation only!

The ADD student ends up lugging every book and every paper for a reason based upon her life's experience. Because she knows she tends to forget things, she copes by putting everything in the bag; because her sense of time and her ability to prioritize is weak, she carries the bag all the time–just in case.

Unfortunately, this coping skill is flawed.

The crammed bag removes the items from visual reference. If and when the student empties the bag, she finds a multitude of items she didn't remember putting in the bag! Also, as time passes and the bag fills, it becomes impossible to find *anything* in this swamp of *everything*.

1. Have more than one book bag/backpack in contrasting colors. Use one bag for morning classes and another for afternoon classes, or have one bag for work to be handed in and another for returned work. Some schools have gone to so-called "block schedules" with longer periods and classes which meet on alternate days; in this situation, two book bags would eliminate a lot of confusion about what to take to Monday's classes versus what to take for Tuesday's classes.

Block A Day

Block B Day

2. One way out of the overflowing bag problem is a mandatory nightly homework assignment: empty the bag and repack it only with the

items needed on the next day. (At first, ADD students will resist, but parents should insist.) Time how long it takes to empty, sort, and repack the bag for several nights, so the student gets an idea of how long it actually takes. (The first night will be the worst!)

Papers which are not immediately needed can be paper clipped according to subject and tacked on a bulletin board or placed in transparent plastic folders, color-coded for subjects.

What Organizer Supplies Work Best For ADD Students?

A great deal of money is spent by well-meaning parents on "organizer supplies" for their ADDers, and, unfortunately, a great deal of money is wasted because the supplies purchased are not "ADD friendly." This situation can be very frustrating to both the parents and the ADD student; the good news is there are supplies which can help ADD people arrange their lives more easily.

One important point: when going shopping for supplies, always take the ADD student along. If he has some input on the items being purchased, he will be more likely to give them a fair trial.

ADDer helps shop for school supplies.

ADD Friendly Shopping List

_____ Colored markers (washable ink)
_____ Pens with several color inks in one barrel
_____ Transparent plastic folders in various colors
_____ Colored file folders
_____ Post-it® notes of several sizes, shapes, and colors
_____ Note pads in funny shapes and bright colors
_____ Dry erase boards and markers
_____ Wire (or clear plastic) baskets
_____ Clear plastic bins with covers
_____ Bulletin boards/colored thumb tacks
_____ Colored paper clips (several sizes)
_____ Folders and folder inserts with pockets
_____ Spiral notebooks (a color for each class)
_____ Notebooks with transparent zip-lock covers
_____ "Fun" desk supplies
_____ "Accordion" files (for dividing big projects
          like research papers into small sections)
_____ Note cards in several colors
_____ Stopwatch/timer
_____ Pocket calendar (week-at-a-glance)

On the other hand, there are also some **supplies to avoid**. These include plain manila file folders, slotted drawer dividers, metal file cabinets, and "loose leaf" notebooks–or, as one ADDer calls them, "lose-leaf" notebooks.

In particular, ADD students often **despise** the classic "3 Ring Binders" for a number of reasons. First, they require "fiddling with" and slow down the process of stashing papers. They also make a lot of noise and can "snap" at the person trying to use them. (One ADD adult we know refers to them as "the metal jaws of death.") Finally, people who are easily bored with routine find poking spikes through holes as interesting as watching grass grow!

ADDers usually prefer folders or folder inserts with pockets for fast and easy storage of papers. These folders (see picture) can be purchased in colors, with each color designated for a certain class or subject.

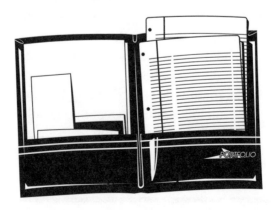

See Time and Space chapter for more tips on organization for Younger ADDers.

TIME TIPS

INTRODUCTION

 How Can An ADD Student Start "Time Training?"

 How Can I Get My ADD Student To Use A Schedule?

 Why Do ADD Students Procrastinate About Homework?

 How Can An ADD Student Learn To Meet Deadlines?

INTRODUCTION

It's About Time!"

Difficulties with understanding and managing time are fundamental problems for ADDers, problems which often lead to personal frustrations and academic disasters. The ADD student doesn't write an assignment's due date, procrastinates about starting, and then turns in inferior work because he rushes to finish at the last minute. Or, the student spends hours on homework that should take less than 30 minutes, dawdling and doodling while staring into space. This apparent lack of "time sense" is often a key element when an ADD student fails to perform at a level commensurate with his intelligence.

Moreover, the "timeless" perspective of ADD can cause a state of personal confusion, of being perpetually "lost." Because the ADD student has no concrete sense of time, she may feel "disconnected" from the pace and rhythms of the real world. Eventually, the student's lack of control in this area may result in a pessimistic "Why bother?" attitude and low self-esteem, both of which can exacerbate a downward spiral of achievement.

In order to resolve these critical time management problems, ADD students and their families must address the issues directly and deliberately, fully recognizing that managing time will not "come naturally" to ADDers. It is also crucial for parents of ADD students who are on therapeutic medications to realize **medication does not "cure" time management problems**. It can improve an ADDer's ability to focus on coping skills (such as the tips offered in this section), but medicine alone will not change behavior patterns, nor will it suddenly endow the student with time awareness.

ADDer's Concept of Time

Understanding how an ADDer views time is crucial for coping with ADD time management problems. First of all, ADDers have no innate conception of time, no "inner clock" by which to measure time. It has been pointed out by ADD professionals that for ADDers, there are two kinds of time: **now** is one kind–and **all other time** is the second. Therefore, to the ADD mind, past, present, and future do not necessarily connect in any obvious pattern, a situation which makes it difficult to use past experiences as a basis for future decisions.

Another difficulty which stems from a lack of time sense is the inability to estimate time. ADDers tend to over and/or underestimate how long it will take to complete specific tasks. If they underestimate, the task seems too trivial to require their immediate attention–so why not wait till later to start it? ("Later" is an example of that second kind of time; for ADDers, "later" never comes!) On the other hand, if they overestimate the amount of time, the task then seems too huge and overwhelming–so why bother to start at all? Both scenarios end up with the same result–the task seldom reaches completion.

Because time confounds and frustrates people with ADD, many of them view time with suspicion or outright hostility. Most ADDers don't wear watches; those who do wear watches consider them more as jewelry than as timepieces. Moreover, ADDers are reluctant to even talk about time issues, and when they do talk about time, their language reveals the fear and loathing they associate with schedules, clocks, and deadlines.

In fact, since it does not fit into their scheme of thinking, many ADDers simply perceive time as being irrelevant. As a rule, ADDers are **task-oriented, not time structured**; the concept of working from "9 to 5" is alien to them. If a task engages the interest of the ADD student, he starts **now** and works on it until the mission is finished or until he collapses from exhaustion, without consideration to the time element. On the other hand, if the task doesn't engage the ADDer's interest or if there is no immediate deadline pressure, the student will avoid beginning the task and will take a paralyzingly long time to complete the work.

For people with ADD, paying attention to time requires conscious effort, an effort which not only drains energy but which also interrupts the rapid flow of ideas and thoughts which form the basis of their natural mental processes. In addition, ADDers are generally independent, anti-authority "free spirits" who see schedules (particularly "grid" style calendars) as restrictive traps designed to destroy their spontaneity and inhibit their creative thinking. From their perspective, time is a threat, one they resist instinctively.

The sad irony is this instinct works against the very gifts the ADDer is trying to protect. Creative abilities are squandered if the ADDer can't devote time to developing his talent. The world gives scant recognition to unfinished songs, incomplete sketches, or novels which don't get beyond Chapter One; great ideas and inventive thinking are only pipe dreams unless time is spent bringing them to reality.

However, many ADDers have learned to manage time without sacrificing their natural gifts, to enjoy the satisfaction of being both creative and productive. Such successes demonstrate that, with deliberate "time training," ADDers can perform to their greatest level of achievement and maintain their individuality.

Time Training Pays Off!

How Can An ADD Student Start "Time Training?"

The first step in "time training" is to increase the student's awareness of time. This process begins with providing visual time references for the student.

1. Take the student shopping for calendars which he finds visually attractive and put them wherever the student "spends time" at home. In addition to obvious places like the student's room or desk, consider some "non-traditional" spots for calendars, such as in the bathroom, near the telephone, in the garage, next to his main exit door, on a car dashboard, on the refrigerator, and near the television.

Note: Avoid the "one-day-at-a-time" type of calendars which require the user to tear off a sheet daily. Although these daily calendars often have cartoons or jokes which ADDers

Avoid Day-At-A-Time Calendars.

enjoy, there's not an ADDer alive who will remember to tear off the sheet each day; this means 99.9% of the time, the student will be looking at the **wrong** date! (In fact, most ADDers will probably read through the whole year's worth of cartoons at one sitting and then never look at the calendar again!) Since ADD students already live on a "one-day-at-a-time" basis, these calendars won't help them develop any long-range time perspective.

2. Take the student shopping for watches and clocks, and, within reasonable budgetary limits, allow her to choose <u>several</u> which appeal to her. We advise trying analog rather than digital watches. (See Time and Space for Younger ADDers.) A watch with an "alarm clock" can be useful; however, parents should be wary of buying watches which are loaded with a number of unnecessary functions. Not only are these timepieces more expensive, they also provide opportunities for distraction as kids "fiddle" with buttons and knobs.

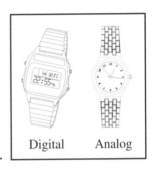

Digital   Analog

The student should wear a watch to school, at scheduled activities, and during "chore times" at home. If the student rebels against wearing the watch during vacation or "free time" days, it may be best to allow for these "timeless" periods. This compromise helps reduce the student's anxiety about time as an inflexible trap.

Place clocks wherever the student needs to be aware of time, places similar to the calendar locations suggested earlier. It is particularly important the student has a prominent clock in the bathroom/dressing areas where he gets ready for school each day.

3. Set up a dry erase or washable marker calendar and designate a specific color marker for

each family member, including parents. It's a good idea to have several markers handy of all the colors, but be sure to have at least two "spares" in the color designated for the ADD student; "I lost the marker" will be the first objection heard from the ADDer.

At the beginning of the week, each family member writes "times to remember" on this family calendar. These times can include appointments, club meetings, "must see" television shows, dinners, parties, dates, and even scheduled "free hours," time specifically set aside for play or for doing nothing at all.

It's particularly important to let the ADD student who is "time training" see that scheduling means more than just obligations, chores and homework assignments. When we introduce schedules to our ADD clients at Brainworks, we often start by having the student schedule only "non-working" fun hours when beginning to work on long-range planning, keeping in mind that for ADDers, **anything past now is considered "long-range" planning.** After practicing the process of scheduling, the student then moves to setting aside time for more serious pursuits, hopefully with a less suspicious attitude toward the process itself.

How Can I Get My ADD Student To Use A Schedule?

For ADDers, a personal "weekly calendar" is one survival tool they must master. However, as we mentioned in the introduction to this sec-

I don't need a calendar.

tion, the first instinct of most ADD students is to reject the idea of using such a tool. In our experiences at Brainworks, our adolescent ADDers often fiercely resist the idea of writing down plans or reminders. Their resistance usually passes through several phases, including denial ("I don't need to write that down because I know I'll remember."), more denial ("OK, I forgot it last time, but I won't forget it next time."), defensiveness ("Are you saying that I'm too stupid to remember that?"), false efficiency ("I don't have time to write stuff down; I'm a busy person!"), rebellion ("You can make me write it down, but you can't make me look at it!"), and identity conflict ("I'm too cool to carry a calendar; that stuff is for nerds.")

Despite this automatic hostility, an ADDer can adjust to using a calendar provided that (1) she perceives it as something she uses and controls, not as something which controls her, and (2) she sees benefits connected with using it. The tips below will help achieve those objectives.

1. Don't buy a "state-of-the-art" top dollar day-time planner designed for grown-up business people and expect an ADD teenager to use it. Such planners are usually massive affairs with lots of divided sections for daily/weekly/monthly plans as well as pages of information ranging from time zones to the phases of the moon.

Avoid giant day-time planners.

First of all, few teenagers will want to haul around a large "dorky looking" notebook from class to class all day. Also, the multitude of sections gives the ADDer too many choices where to write information and thus may actually contribute to his losing track of time; moreover, the surplus of basically useless information not only makes it harder for the ADDer to find the page he wrote on yesterday, it may also serve to distract his attention from what he should be doing. ("Gee, here's a list of the birthstones for each month. I wonder what the stones for all my friends would look like?")

Most parents who have purchased these expensive and elaborate planning folders for an ADD teenager find the teenager will either refuse to use the planner or will manage to lose the planner almost immediately. When the parent gets frustrated, the teen has gained another reason to loathe planners–the calendars are just one more source of pressure and discord.

Instead, parents should take the ADD teen shopping for several small, inexpensive pocket-sized calendar books. The ADDer can choose whatever colors or designs she wants, but the inside of the book should open to show a **full week at a time;** under each day there should be a couple of inches of space, so the student can write several reminder phrases. It's a good idea to buy more than one such calendar (which usually costs under $5 each), so if the student loses one, she can just start using another one. (See sample page 206.)

2. Encourage the student to use a variety of colors in the calendar book. This strategy makes the book more visually appealing, and eventually the student can develop a color coding system,

such as homework noted in green and social plans or fun time marked in red. However, don't impose a color coding system on the student; allowing him to make his own choices leads him to view the book as his property.

3. Students can also have pictures in the calendar book as reminders. Artistically gifted ADDers can sketch their activities with visuals. For example, if the student needs to be at football practice on Tuesday at 5:30, he can draw a picture of a football with the time written on its side. On the other hand, ADDers who aren't as artistically inclined can use "stickers" or pictures cut from magazines or catalogs to create visual reminders.

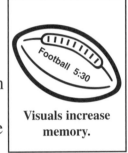
Visuals increase memory.

4. Whenever the student uses the calendar, the act should be reinforced with praise from parents, teachers, coaches, etc. Be sure to point out how the calendar has helped the student control her own life, prepare for activities, and meet obligations. Phrases such as, "I'm glad you remembered to bring home your gym shorts today without my having to remind you," or "When I see you write in your book, it shows you are handling things on your own," help the student

become more aware of the advantages of using the calendar.

5. Stress the flexible nature of planning with the ADD student. In other words, plans should be designed with an eye to possible contingencies if the situation changes. These kinds of adjustments are part of the "real life" nature of planning; for example, a family which has planned a picnic may

Plans need to be flexible.

end up having a "patio picnic" if the weather doesn't cooperate. Or, a trip to the movies might be delayed in favor of an offer to go camping. The key principle in flexible planning is developing the **skill of anticipation** by learning to foresee upcoming events and plan options based on several possibilities. Although this ability is an area of difficulty for ADDers, discussing possible options step-by-step with a designated ADD "coach," or with parents, teachers, and peers will help the ADD student develop foresight. The following sample telephone dialogue illustrates how such a discussion between an ADDer and a "coach" would work.

Coach: What are you planning for this weekend?

ADDer: Well, Friday night I'm going to the foot-

The Coach

The ADDer

ball game, early Saturday morning I'm supposed to go to the library to do some research for my history report, and Saturday afternoon I'm going to play miniature golf.

Coach: Don't you usually get to bed pretty late on football game nights? Getting up early on a Saturday morning to go to the library might be tough if you're tired.

ADDer: Well, I know I need to go, but I also like to sleep. I might be tempted to just stay in bed. Yeah, and the library is so quiet! Sometimes I want to pull a magazine over my face and stretch out when I'm there anyway. Maybe I should go on Sunday.

Coach: Another thing you might want to check on is the weather. It's supposed to rain Saturday afternoon through Sunday morning.

ADDer: Then I won't get to play golf! What a drag! Everything's going to go wrong this weekend! I never get to have any fun!

Coach: Stop and take a look at your schedule for a second. I'll bet you can figure out a way to arrange a few things.

ADDer: Hmmm. I could check with my friends and see if they could play on Sunday afternoon as a back-up plan. Yeah, then I could sleep late on Saturday, and I could be in the library Saturday during the rainy weather.

Coach: And if the weather changes and it doesn't rain?

ADDer: Then I'll sleep late Saturday, play miniature golf, and then go to the library. Hey, Todd was going golfing with us, and he needs to go to the library for his report, too. Maybe after the game, he'll go with me, and we can help each other find stuff.

Coach: Those are good plans. Now all you need to do is figure out some time estimations. How late is "late" when you sleep in?

ADDer: Usually about 10:00-10:30. Any later and I wake up from hunger!

Coach: So when will you start the golf?

ADDer: Well, by the time we all get there and get signed up–probably about 11:30. Maybe noon.

Coach: And how long will it take you to play the round?

ADDer: If there are no ties, it should take about an hour to an hour and a half. If two people tie, we usually play one more hole for "sudden death." That will take an extra fifteen minutes or so.

Coach: So about when should your game end?

ADDer: No later than 1:30. Then Todd and I will go to the library...

Coach: Straight to the library?

ADDer: Come to think of it, we'll probably be hungry. Maybe we should go get some food first so we won't be starving.

Coach: How long will lunch take?

ADDer: The way Todd eats??? Probably an hour. So, we should get to the library by about 2:30...

Coach: How long do you think you'll be in the library?

ADDer: However long it takes. I have no idea.

Coach: It might be best to make an estimation and set a time goal. That way you'll concentrate on getting things done and can finish faster.

ADDer: Oh, I see. Well, I need to find two books and two magazine articles...I'll bet I can do that in less than an hour! So if it takes me thirty minutes to walk home...I'll tell my folks that I'll be home by about 4:00.

Coach: Sounds like you're going to get to have some fun after all.

ADDer: Yeah–no matter what the weather decides to do! I better call Todd and the others and check with them on Plan A *and* Plan B!

Note that in the discussion above, "the coach" is **not** telling the student what to do or **when** he should do things; the student makes a series of decisions and makes notes in his own calendar book. Because the student sees the schedule in this light, the calendar becomes a means of personal control, a reflection of independence rather than restriction.

Why Do ADD Students Procrastinate About Homework?

Dealing with homework is one of the universal problems of ADD students. Some of them never finish their homework; others never even start the assignments. The basis of this problem lies in two areas. First of all, many ADDers possess above average intelligence, which presents a classic case of "mixed blessings." ADD students are often so bright they are able to get by and make passing grades without doing homework–at least for a while.

Homework is like bodybuilding.

However, somewhere in their academic career (often in middle school, sometimes later), they inevitably reach a breakdown point where having natural "smarts" doesn't do the trick anymore, and they **must** do homework in order to make a passing grade. Unfortunately, they have never developed the "homework muscles" of personal responsibility and focused concentration; these students have not habituated themselves to homework assignments.

The second problem with homework relates

School's out!

to time awareness and estimation. Having just spent eight hours in school feeling bored and restless, the ADDer escapes into "free time twilight zone" as soon as the last bell of the day rings. Indeed, leaving the tight structures of school time for the realm of unplanned time *is* like entering another dimension for the student. To begin a homework assignment would mean sacrificing this dimension of unregulated freedom, perhaps giving up the only part of life which the student sees as belonging to him. The **"all-or-nothing"** perspective of the ADDer leads him to treat reality as **all work or all play,** with no room for compromise. To the ADD mind, "doing homework" is an open-ended task; once it's started, it could go on forever! Therefore, the best way to protect one's free time is not to start this (apparently) endless assignment.

Of course, the irony is that the procrastinator never really gets "free time" at all. The time

ADD Quick Tips

spent avoiding homework is tainted by guilt and, eventually, by failure. As parents complain and teachers pressure, the student's peace of mind is disrupted; the next thing he knows, he is spending most of his "free time" worrying about what isn't getting done. The procrastinator's "escape" has become another trap!

Estimate and time the homework.

In order to overcome procrastination, the student needs to treat homework assignments as requirements, not as options. He must understand the **purpose** of doing work outside of class. In addition, the student needs to increase his awareness of how long tasks actually take and to balance work with true free time—time which belongs to him without guilt. The tips below can help the student develop better home-work skills.

1. For **every** homework assignment, the student should estimate in writing how long it will take to complete the assignment. For example, if there are twenty math problems, he should time how long it takes him to do two problems, then use that estimation to project how long it will take to do the rest of the

LOG SHEET			
Date	Assignments	Estimated Time	Actual Time

problems. Then he should time the work and see how accurate the guess was. (This information can be written on the student's calendar or on a separate "log" sheet of paper.)

2. Since ADDers often work best in "short bursts," homework time should be set up on that basis. Set a timer and tell the student that she has **only** ten minutes to work on vocabulary before she has to stop. (Avoid saying "You must work for **at least** ten minutes.") Then switch to another assignment for ten minutes. If necessary, she can return to her first task for another "short burst." (Many of our clients at Brainworks are surprised by how much they can accomplish in a ten or fifteen minute time span.)

Avoid "homework marathons" in which the student must sit and work until the task is completed; hours later, the bored student will probably be only halfway done, and the parent playing "homework cop" will be frustrated. Homework time should have clearly defined, realistic limits appropriate to the age of the child. A general rule of thumb on homework time used at Brainworks is:

"Homework Cop"

Primary/elementary grades = 30-45 minutes
Middle/junior high school = 45-60 minutes
High school = 1-2 hours

Of course, these times will vary depending on the school, the types of classes being taken, etc. However, if a student consistently spends more time than these guidelines indicate, the situation should be examined for other factors which could be inhibiting the student's progress, such as having a learning disability.

3. More than most other students, ADDers need to comprehend the **purpose** of homework, and teachers and parents should frequently reinforce the function of out-of-class assignments. Remember: In the student's mind, he understood the information when the teacher explained it during class; all this homework is just "busy work" as far as he is concerned. However, the student should be reminded regularly that there is a difference between understanding something in class and practicing it independently, and in that difference lies the distinction between quick comprehension and long-term memory. Therefore, homework provides the student with a chance to apply the knowledge as well as check for mastery of the material involved.

In other words, the student should not only be able to explain **what** the assignment requires, but also **why** it is important to do the work.

Homework will show
if I'm ready to go solo.

• On one level, the answer is that homework grades figure into the grade average. For each class in which the student has homework, parents should ask the student if he knows exactly how much of a percentage homework grades "count" in his final

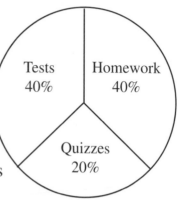

Find out how much homework counts.

grade. If he doesn't know, he should ask the teacher and write this percentage on Post-it®notes inside his folder or textbook and near the spot where he normally studies for the subject.

• It's also a good idea to review the actual effect of not taking time for homework. For example, if homework assignments equal 40% of the overall grade average, the student should be aware she can make straight A's on every test and **still fail** the class. **DO NOT ASSUME** the student can draw this conclusion on her own; sit down with the student and use a calculator to show her the numerical results of not doing homework.

• Also, students should be aware that homework assignments are often designed to present information in small amounts which will eventually be put together to create a larger mastery test. Although this pattern of instruction may seem obvious to teachers and parents, it is precisely the type of long-range connection which many ADD students may not make on their own.

• On another level, the answer to the ADD student's "Why do homework?" question involves what skill or information is being imparted through the homework. In other words, what knowledge will be demonstrated if the student is able to execute the assignment successfully? Have the student explain this purpose aloud to his ADD coach, teacher, or parent.

4. If the student stalls about starting the homework assignment, time how long it takes him to begin. Call his attention to these times by writing them on his calendar or time recording sheet.

GOAL

**Doing homework is a major step
toward making good grades.**

How Can An ADD Student Learn To Meet Deadlines?

First of all, we must begin with the premise that ADDers **can** and **should** learn to meet deadlines. If a person doesn't respond to deadlines, due dates, or other commitments, the end result will be a lifelong stream of academic, personal, and professional failures which ultimately will diminish the individual's sense of self-worth, confidence, and pride.

Unfortunately, well-meaning attempts to provide modifications for ADD students sometimes make it difficult for the ADDer to learn this life skill. One of the standard  modifications for learning disabled students is that of "extending deadlines" and accepting late work; however, this approach is **NOT** a proper strategy for most ADD students.

Giving students more time to complete

assignments is a proper modification if the students process slowly or have serious handwriting difficulties. Of course, some ADDers can also have problems in these areas, but as Dr. Sam Goldstein has pointed out, ADD is primarily a **disorder of consistency, not of ability.** Therefore, routinely extending deadlines (which reinforces inconsistent behavior) represents the worst possible approach for these students.

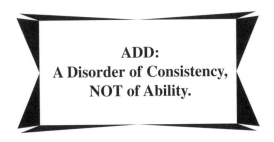

**ADD:
A Disorder of Consistency,
NOT of Ability.**

By and large, people with ADD work best under pressure. Extending a deadline does not give the ADD student more time to work; it gives her more time **not** to work. It also encourages the pattern of procrastination, a trait which eventually becomes a tragic lifestyle for the ADD adult who cannot meet work obligations, file income taxes, pay bills, or arrive at social engagements **on time**. Parents or teachers who let the ADDer "off the hook" in terms of allowing the student to miss deadlines need to ask themselves a crucial question: "In twenty years, will this child's employer,

IRS agent, utility company, or spouse be willing to let him or her off the hook?"

On the other hand, meeting deadlines can give a student confidence about his ability to perform and create a greater sense of independence. The tips below provide strategies to help ADDers learn this vital skill.

1. ADDers don't need extended deadlines; they need shorter, more immediate deadlines. For example, on Monday, a teacher gives the entire class 40 vocabulary words to define and says the work is due on Friday. However, the due date schedule for the ADD student is modified. This student **must** hand in 10 words on Tuesday, 10 more on Wednesday, and so forth. (The **first time** one of these shortened deadlines is missed, parents should be contacted immediately and informed.) DO NOT GIVE THE STUDENT A "SECOND CHANCE" TO FAIL!

Shorten Deadlines				
Mon.	Tues.	Wed.	Thurs.	Fri.
10 + words	10 + words	10 + words	10 = words	40 words

2. Parents and teachers should work together on establishing a concrete list of consequences for missing deadlines. Saying, "You'll be in big trouble if you don't finish that research paper on time," is not only too vague to be meaningful for an ADD student, but it also connotes enough mysterious danger to tempt the student into testing the threat and discovering what "big trouble" could be.

Also, as Gilbert and Sullivan once wrote, "Let the punishment fit the crime." Separate consequences into "major and minor" transgressions, according to the nature of the deadline missed. (See Personal Pointers Chapter for more information on how to handle consequences.)

3. If a student chooses not to do an assignment, he should nevertheless be required to hand in a sheet of paper with his name and the date on it. At the top of the paper, the student should write, "I did not hand in (Fill in the assignment)," and sign the paper.

The reasoning behind this requirement is not punitive. In the course of working with ADD students, we have often observed the striking reality that many of our clients **preferred getting a zero** on a paper they didn't hand in rather than give the teacher a partially completed or low quality assignment which could earn a grade of 50-60.

Although this makes no numerical sense, it makes a great deal of psychological sense to these students. In their minds, when they get a paper back with a grade of 60, they made a bad grade. When they hand in nothing and get a grade of zero, they do not receive a paper back from the teacher with a bad grade. Therefore, the zero does not represent a bad grade; the **zero is a non-existing grade!** When students hand in a signed sheet of paper acknowledging they did not turn in the assignment, the teacher can return the paper as a tangible reference point.

4. When other students are given **in-class time** to work on homework assignments, the ADD student should be required to hand in what he has accomplished before exiting the classroom. The remainder of the assignment can be finished at home, then stapled to the in-class section the next day. (Teachers can even opt to grade the in-class portion separately, and then average that grade with the at-home work.)

This strategy helps ADD students stay focused on doing the work during the time given them in class—time which might otherwise be wasted because most ADD students feel absolutely no imperative to start tomorrow's homework "early" (i.e. "today").

5. Teachers should **NOT** accept **late work** from ADD students for "partial credit." By allowing this option, teachers provide the student with an opportunity for what we at Brainworks call "the

NO LATE WORK!

FINISH

successful failure." This situation occurs when the ADD student hands in a brilliantly written "A+" essay, perhaps the best paper in the entire class—which ends up with a grade of 60 because it was turned in two days late. Most of our ADD clients have experienced such disappointing "achievements," and when we ask them why they turned in the work late, their answer is simple: "Because they let us."

Sadly, in this age of fluctuating educational standards, many school districts across the country have adopted policies which require teachers to accept work which is handed in days, weeks, and even months past the due date. (In some cases, school district policies do not allow teachers to give a grade of **zero** for assignments which have not been done; consequently, students can make a grade of 55 just for breathing!)

Parents of ADD students should check their district's policies and the policies of the particular school regarding credit for late work. If the guidelines are similar to those in the above paragraph, parents should strive to have these policies modified so their ADD children will be held accountable for meeting deadlines. Otherwise, a child who is intelligent enough to make excellent grades may end up continuously existing on the thin line between failing and barely passing, an existence which takes a toll on the student's self-esteem and which creates a distaste for academics in general.

6. Another common modification for ADD students which may do more damage than good is the strategy of giving "untimed tests." Again, this modification may be appropriate for some students, but **giving "timeless" exams to people with short attention spans is illogical.** Having an unlimited (and thus unstructured) amount of time to complete a task means it will be harder for the ADDer to stay focused on finishing the test; there is no imperative to concentrate, and there is ample opportunity to let the mind wander.

A proper modification for an ADD student in testing situations would be to break the exam into smaller sections and have the student work on each section in **short "bursts" of 10-30 minutes.** This adaptation not only reflects the optimum performance style of ADDers but also helps the student develop time awareness/estimation abilities. Moreover, the student and teacher can gradually lengthen the time spans of these "bursts" in increments of 3-5 minutes and eventually "stretch" the student's concentration span so the modification will no longer be necessary.

7. When students note deadlines and due dates in their calendar books, some special consideration needs to be given to **where** the notes should be written. As our ADD clients have worked on using their calenders for due dates, we have noticed they sometimes become confused about marking due dates for assignments. For one class, a student would write the homework on the date slot the teacher assigned it,

> **Scheduling things on a calender can tie ADDers in knots.**

but for his next class he wrote the homework pages on the day the work was due. In yet a third class, he wrote the assignment on the day he was planning to execute the work. With such a mishmash of systems, it took almost no time for this youngster to become uncertain about when anything was due!

To reduce confusion about due dates for long-term assignments, we suggest marking important deadlines in three places—on the date the work was assigned, on the date it is due, and on the times the student is going to work on the assignment. (It may be particularly helpful to color-code these two notations with one color for planned work times and another for the actual time the work is due.) Marking only the due date can be disastrous for ADDers since they do not have "natural foresight." As one of our young ADD clients put it, "If you only write it on the day it's due, you won't know about it until it's too late to do it!"

S	M	T	W	T	F	S
		① Book Report Assigned	2 Get Book 180 pages	3 Read 20 pages	4 Read 20 pages	5 Read 20 pages
6	7	8 Read 20 pages	9 Read 20 pages	10 Read 20 pages	11 Read 20 pages	12 Read 20 pages
13	14 Rough Draft	15 Final Copy	⑯ Book Report Due	17	18	19

(Note: row 2 — the "Read 20 pages" entries: under T(8), W(9), T(10), F(11), S(12).)

This process of "double entry" calendar maintenance also provides students with practice in time estimation and goal-setting. After the student marks the due date, she must then "back up" in time to note when she should begin working on the assignment, and in order to do that, she must estimate and target times to work. Keep in mind that developing these abilities will take a certain amount of trial, error, and adjustment; with practice, the student can learn to handle time independently.

For more time tips
see Time and Space
for Younger ADDers.

STUDY STRATEGIES

INTRODUCTION

 Under What Conditions Does An ADD
Student Study Best?

 What Strategies Can Help The ADD
Student In The Classroom?

 How Can ADD Students Learn To Listen?

 What Study Strategies Work And Don't
Work For ADD Students?

 How Can ADD Students Do A Better Job
With Major Writing Assignments?

INTRODUCTION

Study Strategies

As the ADD student grows and proceeds through the stages of education to middle and secondary school, the number of subjects multiply, the classrooms get more crowded, the assignments get longer, and the sheer logistics of moving textbooks and other materials from room to room becomes increasingly complex. Faced with these difficulties, some ADD students may begin to feel they are fighting a lost cause and may "give up" their efforts to achieve academic success. This despair destroys their self-esteem and may lead to a general sense of hopelessness about other areas of their lives.

However, this depressing scenario is not necessarily inevitable. Academic success is possible, as the achievements of thousands of outstanding ADD students demonstrate. ADDers can learn and can produce; but in order to do so, they may have to employ methods and strategies suited to their particular learning styles. They may also need to focus more consciously and deliberately than their non-ADD peers on improving areas of weakness, such as listening skills or test-taking. Finally, they should learn to develop and utilize the ADD characteristics which may actually provide them with advantages, including creativity, spontaneity, innovation, and energy. The tips in this section can help make the road to scholastic achievement less rocky.

ADDers can overcome obstacles better when they use their talents and gifts.

Under What Conditions Does An ADD Student Study Best?

The standard response to this question has traditionally been "find a study area free of distractions." However, this vague description doesn't provide parents or students with enough information to be of much practical use.

First of all, it's important to define the term "distraction." Most people who do not have ADD tend to identify distractions very differently from people who have the condition. A non-ADDer might describe a "distraction-free area" as a closed space without noise, windows, or pictures. To a person with ADD, that description sounds more like the inside of a coffin than a study area!

Many ADDers have difficulty maintaining concentration in silent, confined spaces with no visual stimuli. One of the hallmark characteristics of ADD has long been described as "a low tolerance for boredom," but in reality, the ADD mind seldom reaches the point of boredom. When threatened with monotony, the ADD mind rapidly leaps to ideas and thoughts which are more attractive and stimulating. Therefore, putting an ADD student in an empty room with "no distractions" on the theory that it will give him "nothing to do except his homework" may actually backfire. Prompted by the lack of stimuli in the immediate surroundings, many ADDers will simply (and automatically) slip into daydreams.

Other reactions may be more extreme. One of our adult clients related his experience with the "distraction free area" his elementary school tried with him:

"As a child...I just could not concentrate, memorize, or work on something that did not interest me. Teachers believed the best way to help me concentrate was to put me in a little room with nothing on the walls and a window which was covered with butcher paper. They soon found out this did not work. For several days, they told me they were not going to listen to my excuses about why I couldn't stay in there any longer. I finally walked up to the teacher, and before I could say I was sick, I threw up on the floor."

This "solitary confinement" approach to a study area eventually reinforces the student's loathing of homework and studying, and the more dreadful a task becomes to an ADDer, the more likely he is to avoid it. The goal, then, is to create a study area which enables a student to focus on his task and to perform at his maximum level while simultaneously providing an attractive and comfortable environment.

In order to achieve this goal, it is necessary to analyze what constitutes a distraction for the student and to determine under what conditions the student performs best. The tips below offer some guidelines for this process.

1. Establish what distracts the student. As unobtrusively as possible, observe the student during several homework sessions and note what factors interrupt her attention. Is she more distracted by noises inside or outside the house? Does the sound of the fan bother her? If someone walks by, is it sound or motion which catches her attention? Is she more distracted by sudden sounds like

A Possible Distraction

ringing telephones or by family members having a lengthy conversation down the hall? Does she shift position or fidget more readily in certain chairs or at certain desks? Is the student better able to concentrate and stay alert in a warm or a cool room? Does she frequently get up to get a drink of water or something to eat?

2. Once the specific distraction "triggers" are determined, the parent **and** the student should use this information to "design" a study area for minimum distraction. For one person, the plan might involve converting an interior room (or even a large "walk-in" closet) with a door, furnished with nothing but a bean bag or comfy chair, a floor lamp, and a lap board; for another person, the best study arrangement might be sitting at the kitchen counter on a stool with a ready supply of snacks or cold drinks. Some ADDers can do their homework on a computer, but for those who are heavily "into" computer games, a computer console may represent the worst possible distraction. These students often cannot concentrate if they're even in the same *room* as the computer.

Parents should be sure the student has input in setting up the study area, but parents should also make sure the student keeps the purpose of the area (better concentration and increased production) as the main consideration.

ADDers help design their own study areas.

3. The study zone should be exclusively dedicated to the process of homework, and students should not pursue free-time activities (playing games, talking on the phone, etc.) in the study area.

4. Some factors involving study zones deserve special **"ADD friendly"** considerations. These elements include:

Noise levels

Many ADDers find it difficult to work in a "quiet" area either because the silence itself is a distraction, or because it can seem to intensify noises which would otherwise be unnoticed. For example, in testing situations, ADDers have reported that seemingly insignificant sounds (clocks ticking or ventilation fans) can disrupt their thought processes.

Headphones can muffle sound.

Of course, this reaction is by no means universal. Some ADDers may require a condition as close to silence as possible to maintain concentration. (For these individuals, wearing noise-muffling headphones is often helpful.) However, a number of ADDers prefer to have some form of "white noise" in their study areas as a "cushion" against interruptive noises such as conversations, telephones ringing, traffic sounds, and so forth.

Some forms of "white noise" are better than others. For instance, music usually makes a better "sound background" than television. Following the action of a television show makes a stronger

Good "white noise"– Mozart Instrumentals

demand on a person's attention; even more distracting are television commercials which not only manipulate sound levels to shock the ears but which are written and designed to target short attention spans. Also, playing a familiar tape or CD is preferable to tuning in a radio station with commercials, disc jockey chatter, and an unpredictable play list of songs which may trigger distracting thoughts ("Hey, that's the song I always heard at the swimming pool last summer...").

Other "white noise" options include tapes offering selections of instrumental music to enhance concentration while studying. Most of these tapes contain works by Mozart, Rossini, Bach, and other classical composers, complex music which studies have shown can stimulate specific areas of the brain which involve memory, focus of attention, and rate of production. (Interestingly, research also shows that music styles dominated by repetitive bass notes, such as some forms of rock music, can actually "numb" some of the brain's thought processes and impede mental activity!)

Although most teenagers won't be very enthusiastic about listening to Beethoven and Chopin, parents should encourage youngsters to give this "study tool" a fair trial. For example, set aside a couple of 15-20 minute study periods and have the student read, study, or work math problems while listening to rock or "rap" music and have him evaluate his progress through timings, scores, quizzes, or the amount of material covered. Then have him work on similar exercises while using the study tapes and compare the results. If the student sees a benefit, he may be convinced to employ this relatively painless study aid.

Beethoven

Lighting

Some ADD students report they are

better able to maintain concentration by using a high-intensity beam study lamp in an otherwise dark or dim area. The direct beam highlights the book or materials on which the student is focusing while the surrounding dimness inhibits visual distractions.

Design

Most ADDers prefer less formal settings for work than the traditional straight-backed chair and desk arrangement. An ADDer might do his best work lying on the floor with his feet propped on a chair or sprawled on an over-stuffed couch with books piled on either side of him. Even though parents may cringe at such postures because they don't "look studious enough," keep in mind that the point is to get the work finished, not to "look good," and students often work best when they are comfortable—even though they might not appear comfortable to the non-ADD eye.

What Strategies Can Help The ADD Student In The Classroom?

A few simple adjustments often help ADD students function more efficiently in the classroom. Parents should review the tips below with their child's teacher(s) as well as ask the instructor(s) for any other suggestions to improve the student's performance. If a tip is used in class, the instructor(s) need to provide feedback regarding the effectiveness of the strategy in case the tactic needs to be adjusted.

1. Classroom seating arrangements can be a crucial factor for ADD students. Given a free

Seating arrangements are crucial factors for ADDers.

choice in the matter, an ADD student probably will end up sitting in the back of the room, often in a corner. Teachers sometimes interpret this choice as an expression of hostility, contempt, or indifference on the part of the student. However, this conclusion may not be an accurate reading of the student's behavior.

Because ADDers are visually oriented, they tend to prefer sitting where they can see the entire scope of the room at once. Moreover, they may simply be more comfortable sitting there for the same reason gamblers in the Old West felt better sitting with "their backs to the wall"— no one can sneak up from behind!

Despite the obvious appeal of the back of the classroom, this seating choice is **not** one an ADD student should be allowed to make. The "panoramic" view from the back of the class may be more visually stimulating, but it is also more loaded with potential distractions. Also, having one's "back to the wall" may be too comfortable; the student's lack of vigilance could lull him away from the dynamics of the class.

One point to keep in mind is that adjusting the student's seat doesn't automatically

ADDers need to sit near the "point of action."

mean moving the ADDer as close to the teacher's desk as possible, although that is the stereotypical expectation to the situation. In today's schools, teachers seldom conduct class from behind their desks; indeed, the desk area may be used for little more than record keeping and storing papers. In reality, the student should sit near the "point of action" in the classroom, a spot which may be the overhead projector screen, the chalkboard, or perhaps a lecture podium—wherever most of the learning actually takes place. Also, ADDers should sit in the front row if possible; this placement gives them a view uncluttered by the movement of a classmate's bobbing head and puts them as close as possible to the action point.

When considering seating options, teachers of ADD students should keep some guidelines in mind. First of all, ADDers perform better at independent seat work when using a solo desk rather than sharing space with several others at a large table. If students at solo desks have problems with visual distractions, teachers should supply cardboard "study carrels" for each desk. These mini barriers are easily made by cutting cardboard boxes to form a three-sided shield, or they can be made by folding poster board sheets into the appropriate shape. Students should be allowed to "decorate" these carrels to personalize them and make them more appealing for the youngsters. (Teachers should remember to set clear guidelines for what constitutes "acceptable" decorations.)

Study carrels cut down visual distractions.

2. On the other hand, ADD students may study best for exams when working with one or more "study buddies." Since they are often people-oriented, ADD students retain more information when the review process includes discussions or "oral quizzes" within a group format.

ADDers may study well with a "study buddy."

Another classroom seating issue to consider involves the students who sit near the ADD student. Statistically speaking, an average classroom with thirty students could contain at least two to three ADD students; realistically speaking, teachers have sometimes had to deal with classes which contained a much larger percentage of ADD students. Given a choice, these ADDers will probably huddle together in one of the back corners of the room and proceed to develop distraction to an art form. As many wise teachers have discovered, ADDers should not be allowed to form clusters; if possible, they should be surrounded by diligent, attentive non-ADDers who possess a high level of tolerance!

Teachers should not hesitate to experiment with shifting an ADD student's seating placement, but they should always make it clear to the student that the changes are being made to enhance concentration and improve classroom performance (i.e. prevent the ADDer from missing important information and failing the course). If the first seating adjustment doesn't accomplish the purpose over a specific time

Change the ADDer's seat placement to enhance concentration and improve performance.

period (perhaps one full week), teachers should try moving him to another spot. In fact, some teachers of both ADD and non-ADD students shift all the seating assignments in their classes every few weeks to avoid boredom and to expose every student to as many combinations of peers as possible.

3. One of the best ways to get the cooperation of the ADDer is to involve the student in the process. If the student wants to sit in a certain spot, the teacher should specify what behaviors will keep him there and what behaviors will result in losing the seat. The student should "sign off" on a plan similar to the following: "I can continue

sitting at my seat of choice if I can focus and maintain attention when asked. However, if I go off task, the teacher will give me a private signal to move quietly to the alternate spot she has selected. If I have to move more than twice in a week, the alternative desk automatically becomes my seat for the rest of the week."

4. Teachers can reinforce organizational structures by giving students a weekly grade for maintaining class notebooks with assignment calendars, class notes, handouts, and returned papers. When a student fails a notebook grade, teachers should contact parents **immediately.** Waiting until the end of the grading period to call attention to this problem area will mean the ADD student not only misses a great deal of content information, but the "lag time" also allows the disorganization pattern to flourish unchecked.

Grading notebooks can provide organizational structures ADDers need.

5. At the beginning of the school year, parents should check into the possibility of having two sets of textbooks issued to the student—one set for the student to use at school and another set to be kept at home. This arrangement eliminates the possibility the student will either forget a

textbook or bring the wrong book home, and it will also "lighten the load" of the student's back-pack. This accommodation is particularly appropriate for ADD students entering middle school or high school. In these cases, the double set arrangement could be proposed as a short-term measure until the student settles into a regular routine in the new environment. (Parents may have to contact the publishers and purchase these textbooks.)

6. ADD students usually have problems with lengthy, repetitious assignments, particularly if they perceive the exercises as being unchallenging or routine. Given such an assignment, they may quit working on it when they are only halfway finished; even if every problem they worked is correct, they will still receive a failing grade. If an instructor can gauge the student's mastery of a concept or information with 25 problems instead of 50, the chances of an ADD student finishing the assignment and making a passing grade may be greatly improved.

The focus on repetitious assignments should be proving mastery of the concept.

However, students can learn to deal with lengthy, repetitious assignments by breaking them into "short burst" efforts. Our ADD clients at Brainworks often produce better quality work in four 15 minute sessions than in one straight hour, and in the end, ADDers will also be less fatigued by four short sessions than by one sustained study period. Also, students with homework in more than one subject area should rotate their efforts from one assignment to the other when they begin to feel bored.

7. Students should track how much time they spend on each homework assignment. Recording this data not only helps them practice time estimation, it may also help document the need for assistance or modification in subjects which require unusual amounts of homework time and effort.

Study Log			
Date	Assignments	Estimated Time	Actual Time

8. Teachers should consider spending some class time at the start of the school year helping

students become familiar with the parts of their textbooks, such as indexes, glossaries, appendices, map sections, chapter divisions, illustrations, etc. Many ADD students "get lost" within the pages of their texts, and a preliminary scouting session helps orient them. The student may also be surprised by how much can be gleaned from a textbook chapter without reading it verbatim merely by scanning the topic headings, reading information under illustrations, and noting words in bold italic print.

Teachers might even set up a "Textbook Scavenger Hunt" game for the class. Students are given a list of questions which require them to locate items in various parts of the book. (For example: "What is the first word in the "m" section of the index? How many chapters are in Unit Three?") The first student to locate correctly all the information wins!

Textbook Scavenger Hunt

Tour the textbooks early in the year.

9. Many teachers now practice "selective grading" by choosing to evaluate only a representational sample of their students' work instead of grading every single assignment. While this

method has been proven to be an effective means of assessment, teachers should be careful not to fall into a predictable pattern of choosing what will be graded. ADDers who realize the instructor only picks up the homework on Friday will only work on those assignments and will ignore the homework assigned on Monday through Wednesday. Unfortunately, because sequenced instruction involves building upon past knowledge, the student who skips assignments will eventually be unable to execute the Friday assignment because of the "gaps" in his knowledge.

Homework
COUNTS!

Instructors should make sure their selections of papers to grade are random and unpredictable. They should also regularly remind students of the relationship between each assignment—including the ungraded ones—and mastery tests. **DON'T ASSUME STUDENTS UNDERSTAND THIS CONNECTION!** At Brainworks, we frequently discover students who are completely unaware that the information presented in Monday's homework assignments relates to the major test on Friday; they perceive the zero on the homework and the 50 on the test as two unrelated incidents. Teachers and/or parents may have to review tests and homework assignments with the ADD student and point out the specific connections.

Teachers should also be cautious about grading an ADD student's homework based on "effort" rather than content. If the student knows that the teacher will "grade with a glance," he will not put his best effort into the work. Grades based on merely making an attempt to work math problems or to write sentences for vocabulary words will not provide evaluation of student mastery; that evaluation will come in the form of "test day disaster."

How Can ADD Students Learn To Listen?

Many ADD students have problems processing auditory information because of their sporadic attention. As a result of either external distractions or of the internal interruptions of their

Most ADDers have a listening problem.

own stray thoughts, they may recall part of the information they hear, but they may not "capture" many of the key points. This "listening deficit" becomes most apparent when ADDers have to recall sequenced information which is given to them verbally, such as a teacher giving step-by-step instructions for an assignment.

In particular, taking class notes from lectures may seem almost impossible for ADD students. In his video, **"Answers to ADD: The School Success Tool Kit,"** Dr. John Taylor points out that taking notes requires the simultaneous application of several skills, including sustained attention, cognition, translation, handwriting, and immediate memory – none of which can be considered ADD "strong points." Learning to listen is a crucial life skill, and there are several methods ADD students can employ to improve their auditory recall.

1. When teaching the student to listen to verbal instructions, start small and work up to more complex sequences. Several times a week, parents (or an ADD coach) should spend about five minutes helping the ADD student train for listening to sequences. The student should listen while the trainer reads a set of steps; after listening to the entire sequence, the student then executes the task. At the start of the training, the student should work on 2 and 3 step sequences. (For example, "Open your backpack and get out your math book" is a 2 step sequence while "Open your backpack, get out your math book, and open the book to page 73" is a 3 step sequence.) Keep track of how accurately the students respond and reward perfect scores with profuse praise!

Sequencing
1. _____
2. _____
3. _____
4. _____

Training the ADDer to listen to sequential directions is imperative.

Over time, the number of steps in each sequence can be gradually increased, and the student will become a more alert listener. However, parents and teachers should realize that it is wishful thinking to believe ADDers of any age can execute a series of detailed verbal instructions without being trained to do so.

2. ADDers often get frustrated with verbal instructions because they try to memorize the **exact words** being spoken, a tactic which practically insures a communication breakdown. Almost immediately, the mind becomes "overloaded" with semantic details since the person's mental energy is being spent on recall, not synthesis. In other words, some ADDers listen intently to the individual words being spoken, but the big picture "sense" of the process is lost. Additionally, this "total recall" strategy creates an enormous amount of stress; when these ADDers miss a couple of words or a phrase, they may give up hope, refusing to listen further since they've already "messed up."

When giving verbal instructions to an ADDer, teachers or parents should describe the "big picture" behind the task **before** going into the intricacies of each step. Also, if the process being explained can be

Visualizing the "big picture" helps to fit the small details together.

broken into two or three major stages or phases, the

student should become familiar with these divisions before diving into the details.

If possible, instructions should include visuals to illustrate the steps for the student. As an alternative, parents and teachers can encourage the ADDer to visualize executing the process, as if the student

ADDers should create a movie in their heads.

were watching a little movie about following the steps.

3. Always check for eye contact with the ADD student before beginning to give instructions orally. In a classroom, the teacher and the ADD student can employ prearranged words or gestures which signal "pay attention to this information." The same "secret signal" strategy can be used at home. However, such signals should be used sparingly; an adult who signals "pay attention" a dozen times in an hour will quickly "numb" the ADDer's response.

Check to see if the ADDer is paying attention.

Teachers and family members should also be aware that achieving eye contact with an ADDer doesn't necessarily guarantee having the student's total concentration, for many ADD individuals can look as if they're paying rapt attention while their minds roam the universe. (This behavior is particularly true of those ADDers who are not hyperactive.) If teachers or parents believe they have the eyes but not the consciousness of the ADD student, they should ask a simple question, such as "May I borrow a pencil?" or "Is that a new shirt?" to check for presence of mind. (A student who responds by saying "Huh?" may not be as attentive as it appears!)

Find clever ways to teach listening.

4. Use activities which appeal to the student's interests to practice listening for details. For example, if the ADDer likes to cook, read a new recipe aloud while the student prepares the dish. Or, if the student is learning a new game,

family members or friends should read the rules aloud; during the game, players should ask questions of each other to check how much information has been retained. An ADD student who enjoys sports might listen to games, interviews, or score reports on radio or television and then play "anchorperson" by communicating the reports to others.

5. Read newspaper stories aloud to the student to see how much information she can

The newspaper provides opportunities to teach listening for the "5 W's."

capture from listening. Before beginning to read, tell the student to listen for the classic "5 W's" of journalism: Who, What, Where, When, and Why. (Make sure the story is no more than 4 to 5 paragraphs in length and that it is a news story, not an editorial or a feature article.) After the reading, see if she can respond aloud to the "5 W" questions and let her check the article to see how accurate the answers are.

6. It's important to "check for understanding" when giving oral instructions to ADD students, but simply asking "Do you understand what I just said?" is not an effective means of doing so.

When asked this question, most ADDers will nod sweetly and say "Yes" even if they didn't capture the information. Instead, ask the students to repeat or summarize the information aloud in their own words.

Avoid using "yes/no" questions with ADDers.

ADD Quick Tips

What Study Strategies Work And Don't Work For ADD Students?

In general, the most effective study strategies for ADDers involve active rather than passive approaches to learning. Most students employ only one method for studying, a passive process usually described as "looking over" the material. These students study by reading and re-reading the textbook or notes; occasionally, they might stare at a diagram or chart for an indeterminate period of time. This type of "study session" starts the night before the test and ends whenever the students get bored or fall asleep. If they're lucky, they manage to make at least one pass through the review materials before they snooze. Unfortunately, when some students say they've "looked over" the information, they may actually have "overlooked" most of it!

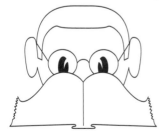

> **Too often ADDers look over the material without really learning it.**

On the next day, the students struggle to hold the "knowledge" in their heads until they take the test; soon after the test, almost all of what they studied disappears from their short-term memory. Most students recognize the brief life span of this type of learning, and many have learned to delay studying for an exam so they won't "lose it" before it's time for the test! Consequently, even students who end up making high scores on tests may exit the class having retained almost nothing of what they "learned."

This method of studying is largely ineffective for any student, but it is particularly useless for ADD students. First of all, since ADDers lack both the focus and the patience to read and re-read chapters or pages of notes several times, the "learn by endurance" component of this study tactic is flawed from the outset. Hyperactive ADDers are physically incapable of sitting still long enough, and ADDers without hyperactivity start daydreaming shortly after beginning the "staring contest" with the textbook.

Secondly, this "looking over" process is open-ended; the ADD student has no idea how long it will take, nor does he have a way to evaluate when

"Learning by endurance" is a killer for the ADDer.

he truly knows the information. Consider this analogy: How motivated would an adult be to take on a job if the boss said, "This project is endless, so your goal is to just work on it till you drop from exhaustion. There's no way for you to know whether you're doing it right or not, but keep working enthusiastically no matter what. And by the way, no one knows if you're going to get paid for this work." Without some end point to the process and without some means of measuring accomplishment, achievement is practically impossible.

Moreover, there is a fatal paradox in the premise of this type of studying. In order to hang on to the short-term information, the student must "wait till the last minute" to begin. On the other hand, the student doesn't know how long it will take to learn the material—so how does he know **when** the last minute will be?

The final disadvantage of passive learning is painfully obvious: when students memorize "just to pass the test," they're not connecting with the educational process. Rather, they are eternally spinning their wheels without making intellectual progress. This dilemma can be particularly devastating to ADD students who typically don't apply effort to tasks they perceive as meaningless or irrelevant.

Far better long-term results can be obtained

through active learning strategies, often with less effort and more fun for the student. **Active learning strategies** require students to manipulate and "interact" with the materials, thus energizing the study process. In **passive learning**, the student is merely an observer; with active techniques, the student is a participant.

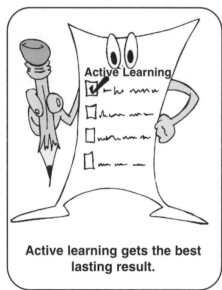

Active Learning

Active learning gets the best lasting result.

Active learning can produce results for any students, but they are especially appropriate for ADD students. Many of the basic elements of active learning, such as color, creativity, and quick feedback, appeal to the natural inclinations of ADDers. These techniques also provide structured approaches to learning; the student establishes a mastery goal, follows specific steps, and tracks the progress made toward the goal. Finally, research indicates that active learning strategies promote long-term recall for lifetime learning.

Two previous publications from Brainworks, **Thinking Smarter** and **Creative Memory**, present a number of active learning activities, and these workbooks show students how to apply these tactics to assignments from science, language arts, and social studies. As our clients work on the lessons, they end up "teaching themselves" how to learn more efficiently; the excellent results they obtain can convince them to abandon the "sit and stare" method which has probably failed them several times in the past. Those techniques which have succeeded most often with the greatest number of our ADD clients are outlined in the following tips.

Student Generated Flash Cards

Purpose: Students learn to translate verbal information into visual flash cards; they learn to evaluate mastery through the "Three Second Rule."

ADD Advantages: The strategy applies creative thinking to the memory process, and it will have special appeal for ADDers who enjoy drawing; however, artistic skills are not as important as creative thinking to this technique.

Visually oriented ADDers will recall information with less effort and will be motivated by the progress they measure. The work can be executed quickly and can be broken into short steps very easily.

Materials: Markers or map pencils (several colors)
3″ x 5″ note cards

Who was the first president of the United States?	washing	ton
side 1	side 2	

Step 1

On one side of the card, the student writes the information to be recalled. This information could be a name, a vocabulary word and/or a definition, a physics rule, etc. (Students with serious handwriting problems can photocopy the written work and paste it on the card.)

Step 2

    On the opposite side of the card, the student sketches a picture which will remind him of the information; students are encouraged to be creative, colorful, humorous, and even silly so long as the image is memorable. This picture may not make sense to anyone else who looks at it, but as long as the connection is clear to the student, the drawing works. If the connection doesn't register with the student, the problem will be apparent during the mastery check step. (NOTE: The student should **time** how long it takes to make each drawing; this data will enable the student to estimate more accurately the time allocations of future study sessions.)

Not Mastered

Mastered

Step 3

    The student employs the "Three Second Rule" to evaluate mastery of the flash card information.

The **Three Second Rule** says if the student looks at the flash card and can recall the information on the other side within three seconds, then the student has mastered that card. The card is placed in a separate pile from the rest of the cards, for there is no need for the student to continue studying what is already mastered. On the other hand, if the student doesn't recall the information within three seconds, the card goes back to the study pile for further review. However, if the student cannot recall the information after several passes, the picture on the card may need to be redesigned for a better "mental" connection. The student should consider using more colors, motion, humor, or "weirdness" to make the connection.

Step 4

After each pass through the cards, the student should count to see how many he knows and how many he still needs to learn. This "score" enables him to track his progress, and when the student goes through the entire pack and identifies all the answers within the three second guideline, the study session is successfully completed.

Webbing for Note Taking

Purpose: Students learn to use a color-coded graphic organizing system to take notes from text materials and review sheets. They learn to evaluate mastery through the "Three Times Rule."

ADD Advantages: This strategy allows ADD students to translate verbal information into a visual study sheet, a format which most ADDers find easier to recall. The color coding appeals to the ADD eye, and it also helps the brain organize the information for long-term recall.

Materials: Plain white paper
Fine point markers (at least 8 colors)
Highlighters (two colors)

Step 1

The student scans the information, noting the central topic, the main ideas, and the supporting details. The most efficient way to do this is to use highlighters to mark the information; for instance, the student could highlight main ideas in green and supporting details in yellow. If the information is from a school-issued textbook or library book, the student should photocopy the pages for highlighting purposes.

Step 2

The student converts the highlighted notes into a webbing graphic. The central topic becomes the core from which all the main idea branches stem; on each stem, the supporting details for the main idea are noted. In addition, each main idea branch is given a color designation.

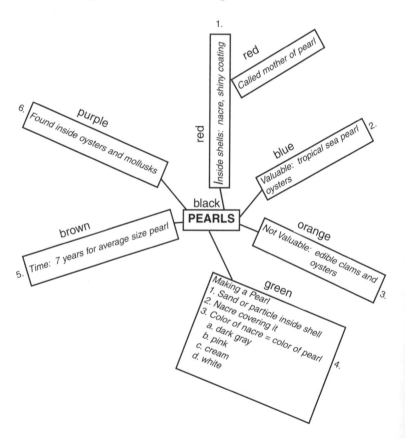

Step 3

The student counts the number of branches of the topic. Then, the webbing is removed from sight, and the student checks his recall by sketching the web on another sheet of paper. When he can draw the web three times from memory, the material has been mastered.

Create Study Notes with Questions

Purpose: Students learn to summarize textbook information by creating sample test questions instead of writing summary statements. They learn to evaluate mastery through either the "Three Second Rule" or the "Three Times Rule."

ADD Advantages: This strategy allows the student to "play teacher" by inventing test questions rather than the usual routine of responding to "end of the chapter" review questions. Thinking of questions is a mentally engaging activity, and as every teacher knows, a person can't create test questions without understanding the answers.

Step 1

As the student reads the textbook, class notes, or review materials, he writes true/false, multiple choice, identification, or fill-in-the-blank test items. At the end of each chapter or unit, he composes short answer and essay questions. The test questions should be modeled on the types of questions most frequently used by the instructor. (This modeling will be difficult at the start of the school year, but over time, the student will develop a general idea of the sort of test items to create.)

It's a good idea to set up a structure for how many questions to write, such as 2-3 per page, 3 per each subheading, or 5 per chapter. The amount will vary depending on the type of material. Also, every time the student turns a page or starts a new sub-heading, he should choose a new color for writing the questions. Changing colors helps keep the student's interest.

Step 2

The student maintains these questions and uses them as a "home-made" review to prepare for the class exam. If he misses any questions, he should return to that page or section for further reading. (Note: If the ADDer works with a "study buddy" in the class, both students can compose test questions, then exchange them for the self-testing.)

Sample Essay Questions

How are Abraham Lincoln and Frederick Douglas alike? *	1. Same time period. 2. Very poor families. 3. Very intelligent and self-educated. 4. Lost their mothers early in life. 5. Worked to end slavery in U.S.
side 1	side 2

*Use the **"Three Times Rule"** for mastery – be able to say out loud these answers three times without "hints" or looking.

Sample Identification Questions

Who was the Confederate general who surrendered at Appomattox? *	Robert E. Lee
side 1	side 2

*Use the **"Three Second Rule"** for mastery – be able to give the answer within three seconds without "hints" or looking.

How Can ADD Students Handle Major Writing Assignments?

Writing assignments can be a daunting task for ADD students, particularly as they enter high school when such assignments become longer and more complicated. ADDers who could write an adequate seven to nine sentence paragraph in the fifth grade may be overwhelmed when they confront the demands of 500 word essays and research papers in their freshman year. Since these papers require much more of students in terms of organization and focused attention, ADD students can easily "get lost" in the process.

The "long-range" nature of major writing assignments also requires that students be able to apply time management as well as composition skills; ADD students who have the ability to handle the actual writing of a five paragraph essay can still be "tripped up" by poor time estimation and planning.

These types of writing assignments require extended organization and focused attention.

500 Word Essay

Research Paper

Finally, even if ADD students manage to write the essay and complete it by the due date, they tend to be the world's worst "proofreaders," for they seldom have the patience or concentration to check details of punctuation, spelling, and usage.

Interestingly, the same strategies which can improve an ADD student's ability to handle longer writing assignments work equally as well with their non-ADD peers. By presenting the writing process as a structured series of distinct steps leading to a final product, a teacher can provide all students with a consistent composition "routine" which they can use across curriculums and throughout their lives. (See Appendix for more information on writing process steps.)

1. Train students to approach writing as a series of steps instead of one sustained effort by evaluating each step as well as the final product. Students should be given separate "check" grades for documenting their brainstorming, for writing the thesis statement, for outlining the paper, for writing the introduction paragraph, etc. as well as receiving a major grade on the finished essay. In other words, the students will have **a series of short-term deadlines** to meet instead of a single long-range (for ADDers a "distant and therefore non-existent") due date. This tactic allows the instructor to monitor the pace of the students'

progress and to detect any problems with topic choice or organization before the expenditure of major effort on writing the first draft.

WRITING PROCESS CHECKLIST

- ☐ Brainstorming
- ☐ Thesis Statement
- ☐ Outline
- ☐ Introduction
- ☐ Paragraph
- ☐ Body
- ☐ Conclusion

---

2. As teachers go through the steps of the writing process, they should model the procedures themselves by brainstorming topics on the overhead, writing sample thesis statements, and so forth. Since holding student interest is crucial, teachers should consider using humorous or even ridiculous topics for their presentations, such as "How to Fail This Class" for analysis papers or "Our Principal versus Superman" for comparison/contrast.

3. When reviewing the format for outlines, instructors can assist the visual learners in the class by presenting examples with designated colors for each level. For example, the first level (capital Roman numerals) in red, the second level (capital letters) in blue, and the third level (Arabic numerals) in green. Or, use color designations for each body paragraph division to note the switch in subject areas.

```
I.    _red_
   A. _blue_
   B. _blue_
       1. _green_
       2. _green_
       3. _green_
           a. _purple_
           b. _purple_
   C. _blue_
II.   _red_
```

4. For each step of the writing process, students should note time estimations and then actually time themselves and document how accurate their predictions were. In future assignments of similar scope, they should use this data for planning.

5. Brainstorming exercises during pre-writing are excellent opportunities for "group work"

assignments. This format offers a greater variety of opinions and ideas concerning possible topic options.

6. Pair students as "writing partners" to review each other's "in-progress" work as they write body paragraphs, revise rough drafts, and proofread final copies. This teamwork is particularly important in the revision and proofreading stages because most students do not read their own work with a "critical eye." More-over, as students re-read their own writings, they often miss errors such as leaving words out of a sentence; since they know what words should be there, their brains will "fill-in-the-blanks."

Some suggestions for "proofreading partners" include:

A. Take turns reading the other person's paper aloud while the author listens for both usage errors and clarity of meaning.

B. Start at the end of the paper and read it backward to check for spelling errors. By removing the words from sentence context, it will be easier for the student to evaluate each word separately.

Use "proof-reading partners" to check for mistakes.

C. Students should allow at least 24 hours

between finishing the final rewrite and proofreading the paper, a strategy which makes it easier to review the work objectively. Teachers can enforce this "cooling off" period by requiring all final copies to be handed in on the due date, then returning the papers 24 hours later to the students for a "last chance" check session.

**"Rewrite options" can
provide a learning experience.**

7. If students are given "rewrite options" for papers which contain good content but which also have too many usage errors to receive a passing grade, teachers should not identify the specific mistakes and provide corrections. Instead, if there is an error on a line, the teacher simply puts a check mark in the margin of that line; if there is more than one error on the line, the teacher makes additional checks. In this way, the student must locate the error, and determine how to correct it, a process that makes a learning experience out of what would otherwise be merely a handwriting exercise.

For additional information on study strategies, see Study Strategies in the section for Younger ADDERS.

PERSONAL POINTERS

INTRODUCTION

Health Issues

 Introduction

 How Can The Diet Of An ADD Child Be Improved?

 What Can Help An ADD Student's Sleep Problems?

 Should My ADD Child Try Therapeutic Medications?

Behavior Issues

 Introduction

 What Can Help "Motivate" An ADD Teenager?

 How Can ADD Teenagers Improve Their Social Skills?

INTRODUCTION

Personal Pointers

As the staff of Brainworks develops remediation plans for our ADD clients, we usually include areas which go beyond the scope of typical tutoring programs. Part of our center's philosophy deals with addressing the needs of "the total person," and to that end, we explore every factor which impacts the lives of our clients. These factors include "personal matters" such as health concerns, motivation, stress management, self-esteem, and behavior modification. In our experience, these issues have an enormous influence on an ADD individual's ability to manage successfully the challenges presented by the condition.

In particular, these areas have a direct connection with the academic performance of ADDers. Many ADD students with low self-esteem and depression began their personal downward spiral as a result of negative classroom experiences, and as their self-confidence drops, their grades will drop still lower, confirming their low opinions of themselves. However, this "vicious cycle" can be broken. As students sharpen their organization and time management skills and practice using alternative study strategies, their classroom performance improves and their self-esteem rises. In other words, success can often be the best possible "therapy," and the tips in this section provide guidelines for making that success more obtainable.

INTRODUCTION

Health Issues Impact The ADDer's Performance

Thanks to the technology of Positron Emission Tomography (PET) and the efforts of researchers such as Dr. Alan Zametkin of the National Institute of Mental Health, we are beginning to understand the biology of ADD in terms of brain chemistry. However, the central nervous system is not the only "physical" component of ADD symptoms; those identified as having the condition tend to share similar experiences with a number of health concerns, including nutrition, allergies, infections, and sleep patterns.

These health factors are sometimes treated as "secondary traits" in the context of ADD studies which focus primarily on the aspects of inattentiveness and impulsivity. Yet, as our clients work on managing ADD successfully, these issues often emerge as much more than "curious coincidences." Health issues have a tremendous impact on the ability of ADD students to perform at their maximum level of capability, and addressing these concerns is fundamental to resolving the practical "survival" challenges they face each day.

How Can The Diet Of An ADD
Student Be Improved?

There are two main problems with the dietary habits of ADDers: (A) what they eat and (B) when they eat it. In terms of the first problem, ADDers are almost universally attracted to the worst sections on the food pyramid chart of the Department of Agriculture. They are "sugar junkies," "grease fiends," and "caffeine-aholics," and the vast majority of our ADD clients at

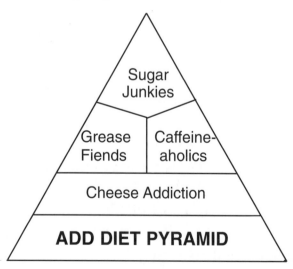

Brainworks freely confess to having what amounts to an "addiction to cheese." The application of terms commonly associated with substance abuse to ADD eating habits is not merely for the sake of melodrama. Rather, the language indicates the effect these foods have on the body chemistry of ADDers and the depth of dependence felt by these individuals.

In some cases, they may be unconsciously "self-medicating" by indulging in these food products. Caffeine-loaded soft drinks, coffee, and tea stimulate flow of the very neurotransmitters needed by the brain for concentration. (In his book **Helping Your Hyperactive Child**, Dr. John Taylor points out that although relatively high doses of caffeine seem to improve attention focus, "its chemical effects on the body seem to be broader than those of the customary medications for ADHD.") The student who chugs a cola between classes may not be alleviating thirst so much as increasing concentration, albeit at a tremendous cost to the kidneys.

Sugar is another substance which ADDers probably use for more than just calories. For years, sugar was erroneously designated as a major cause of hyperactivity, but a number of researchers have discounted such a connection. (About 1-3% of children may have allergic interactions with sugar products which affect their behavior.) What is undeniable is the intense craving ADDers feel for sugar products. If they aren't getting a hyperac-

Sugar offers temporary satisfaction.

tive "charge" out of it, what can explain this powerful yearning for sweets? Studies have shown sugar consumption increases the level of serotonin within the brain; this neurotransmitter is essential for restful sleep and for feelings of well-being. Therefore, the ADD students who demand candy while studying may be instinctively consuming a substance which provides a temporary sense of calm assurance in a stressful situation. However, consuming large amounts of sugar as a "comfort food" is a short-lived tactic which plays havoc with a person's blood chemistry, as anyone who's suffered a post-sugar "crash" can attest.

The passion which ADDers have for cheese

Many ADDers crave cheese.

is almost as powerful as their sweet tooth cravings. Although we don't know of any "cheesy" research studies regarding brain chemistry changes produced by lactose enzymes, our first-hand experience with clients shows they believe cheese is an essential component of almost every meal. Although cheese does provide protein, the high fat content of most cheeses can create more dietary harm than other protein sources, such as legumes, fish, and lean red meat.

ADD students may not even be aware of how much cheese is in their diets. When one of our middle school ADDers swore he didn't eat much cheese, we asked him to list the foods he had eaten the previous day. To start the day, he had an egg and cheese breakfast burrito, and at lunch, he ate 2 slices of cheese pizza. After school, he ate a cheeseburger with some friends, along with some "tater tots" covered with melted cheese. His dinner was spaghetti with sauce, but not the traditional tomato sauce; his "special" recipe called for coating the noodles with butter and (of course) grated parmesan. After looking at this list, the student commented, "Hmmm. I guess I eat more cheese than I thought!"

Compounding the harm caused by poor choices of what to eat is the erratic pattern of when ADDers eat. Most meals are consumed "on the go," resulting in an over-reliance on processed "fast food" items. ADDers in a hurry may skip meals altogether,

ADDers often eat on the run.

and the meal they most frequently avoid is breakfast. Despite the often repeated dictum about "the
most important meal of the day," most of our
clients are repulsed by the thought of putting eggs
or oatmeal into what one teenager called her
"morning stomach." Lunch may also be skimpy; a
crowded lunchroom provides highly-social, talka-
tive ADDers with so many conversational opportunities that their mouths never get a chance to
chew. Finally, some ADD medications may cause
a loss of appetite, so timing medicine becomes a
key factor in whether the student is obtaining anything close to a balanced diet.

However, the nutrition situation isn't entirely hopeless. By making slight changes in diet and
establishing a regular pattern for meals, ADD students can do a much better job of "fueling their
bodies."

ADD Breakfast

1. If the ADD student shudders at the
thought of traditional breakfast foods such as eggs
or cereal, provide some non-traditional alternatives, such as peanut butter/banana sandwiches,
hot dogs (using low fat turkey franks), baked
potatoes, or Philly steak sandwiches. For some

reason, cold leftover pizza is more appealing to the ADD palate than bacon and eggs, but another alternative is to make "mini pizzas" in the toaster oven with English muffin crusts. (Sometimes the novelty of eating such "non-morning" foods will spark the ADDer's natural sense of the bizarre and encourage them to eat breakfast.) As long as the dish provides a source of protein, it's a viable alternative.

2. Keep a supply of "instant breakfast" drinks and food bars available for "quick snacks" throughout the day.

3. Unfortunately, most high sugar snacks (such as cookies and candy) are also highly convenient for ADD students who eat on a "hit and run" basis. Parents can make nutritious foods just as convenient, however, by stocking the pantry with "individual portion" bags of raisins, dried apricots, apples, granola, and other healthy snack alternatives. It's less expensive to buy in quantities and create "homemade" snack bags than to purchase small packages of most food items; this principle also applies to so-called "lunch kits" which provide less than a dollar's worth of sliced ham, cheese, and crackers for a price of $3-5.

Make **healthy snacks** *convenient to the ADDer.*

4. Arrange to have "cheese-free" meals at home as often as possible. Experiment with non-cheese pizzas made at home, using ingredients such as barbequed chicken or sliced steak.

5. If the student is taking stimulant medication, monitor for effects on appetite, and adjust the timing of the dose to have the least impact at the time the school serves lunch. For a few of our clients, lunch schedules can be a problem because their school offers several "shifts" of midday meals, and they may be scheduled to eat as early as 10:40 a.m. or as late as 1:15. Trying to coordinate those lunch times with a medication schedule which calls for dosages every four or five hours can be tough. If the school can possibly adjust the student's lunch shift, it can end up being an important modification. However, if the administrative process for such a change is too awkward, ADD students can cope with the situation by carrying a supply of "healthy" convenient food items (such as granola bars, apples, and peanut butter crackers) in their book bags for premedication "quick snacks" between classes.

ADDers should try to eat before a noon dose of medication.

What Can Help An ADD Student's Sleep Problems?

Sleep disorders can lead to disastrous consequences for an ADD student. First of all, erratic sleep patterns take a visible physical toll. When she stumbles into a classroom with black-rimmed, bleary-eyes and pale complexion, she is obviously in no shape to tackle any academic challenges. After collapsing into a desk, she puts her head down and dozes through the class, managing to miss important information as well as antagonize the instructor. If this behavior continues, the student "disconnects" from the class because she has lost track of what's going on around her, and her eventual failure decreases her self-esteem and reduces her desire to make further efforts.

Erratic sleep patterns can affect school performance.

Sleep issues are not "sideline concerns" in terms of ADD management; without rest, neither the brain nor the body can function efficiently. The following tips may improve the ADDer's ability to "rest easy."

SLEEP LOG	Date :_____ Time	Date:_____ Time	Date:_____ Time
Went to bed			
Fell asleep			
Woke up during night			
Woke up to go to school			

Name_____

1. Track the sleeping patterns of the ADD student over a two week period. For some ADDers, the pattern may be fairly consistent; for example, the student may have trouble falling asleep before midnight, or he may fall asleep at an acceptable time but wake up three hours later and be unable to go back to sleep. Once the nature of the "problem pattern" has been identified, it becomes easier to work on resolving the problem.

Why did the student oversleep? Tracking sleep patterns goes beyond just recording that the student "oversleeps" each morning. This monitoring process should also include an investigation into the **cause of the oversleeping**. In other words, what happened on the night prior to over-sleeping? Did the student "cram" for a test before bedtime? Or did he play video games for an hour before bedtime? How much time elapsed between watching the last television show of the evening and the student's bedtime? Did he eat or drink anything before going to bed? Was he worrying about something after going to bed?

Sleep problems are common with ADDers.

Note: Parents need to be specific when asking questions about these issues. For instance, we have learned **not** to ask an ADD client, "What time did you go to bed last night?" ADDers can be quite literal, and they also tend to lie awake for lengthy periods before falling asleep. Instead, we ask, "What time did you fall asleep?" or "What time was it when you looked at the clock before you fell asleep?" in order to obtain accurate information.

2. Some ADDers have what might be described as "shifting" sleep patterns. One week, they may be unable to fall asleep before 3:00 a.m., but the next week they may fall asleep right after the evening meal. For these individuals,

monitoring may need to continue for longer than a couple of weeks and may involve even deeper investigations of the causes.

3. Establish a baseline measurement for how much sleep the student needs to perform well. Despite the traditional "eight hours a day" adage, the amount of sleep needed varies widely from person to person. When the student has a "success streak" at school or at home, determine how much sleep she averaged during that time. On the other hand, during periods when the student is struggling in class, failing to complete tasks at home, or having conflicts with others, chart how little sleep was averaged.

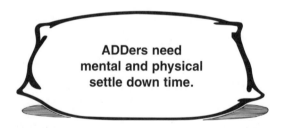

ADDers need mental and physical settle down time.

4. ADDers may have problems falling asleep at the end of a busy day because they frequently "carry the day" to bed with them when they retire. They try to move from an active state to a restful state without providing transitional time for their bodies and minds to "settle down."

One reason some ADDers develop insomnia is due to this tendency; if they don't fall asleep within a few moments after crawling into bed, they quickly grow fidgety and the chance to relax is lost. (In fact, an ADDer who goes to bed earlier than usual in order "to get more rest" before a big day may actually end up getting less sleep than usual!)

ADDers can learn to unwind before bedtime by developing a personal set of "sleep steps" which incorporate methods for relaxing the student's senses and mind as well as his body, and they should be followed in sequence as a regular "sleep routine." The student himself should be responsible for designing the steps, with guidance and input from parents or an ADD coach. Once the steps are decided, the student should commit to following them for a trial period of at least five days in a row, because the key element in this type of process is training the mind and body to anticipate and expect sleep. After the five day experiment, the steps should be evaluated and adjusted if necessary.

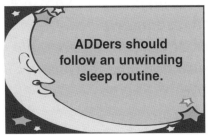

ADDers should follow an unwinding sleep routine.

We use the following guidelines to help our clients set up their rituals; the *italic* statements are an example of one student's sleep plan.

A. First, lower the level of sensory stimulation in terms of the following:

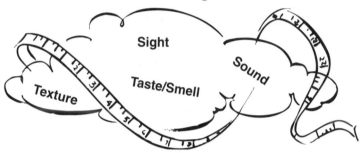

Lower level of sensory stimulation

Texture: *"I will change into my sleep outfit and will make sure there are no books, clothes, or other items on the bed twenty minutes before going to bed."*

Sight: *"I will dim the lights in my room and turn off my computer fifteen minutes before getting into bed."*

Taste/Smell: *"I'll drink a warm cup of peppermint tea with honey and brush my teeth ten minutes before getting into bed."*

Sound: *"I will turn off my radio and will put on my relaxation tape five minutes before getting into bed."*

Warm baths can relax the body.

B. If physical tension is a problem, try taking a warm bath a half hour before bedtime as part of the "calming down" process. (Adventurous souls might even experiment with the so-called 'aromatherapy' bath salts and oils which are designed to promote relaxation.)

C. Practice basic stress management techniques, such as breathing exercises to relax the body and mind. Begin by drawing a slow, deep breath. Hold it for a count of three, and then slowly exhale. Repeat this process at least ten times.

D. Relaxing the mind before bedtime is just as important as relaxing the body. Folk wisdom has long advised "counting sheep" on the theory that the monotony of endless numbers will bore a person to sleep. However, the ADD mind won't respond to this strategy because it rejects boredom in favor of fantasy every time! More success can be obtained by "emptying" the ADD brain than by boring it. Some tactics which have worked for our clients include:

Relax the mind before bedtime.

- Making a list of the day's successes.
- Listening to the "book on tape" version of favorite (and familiar) childhood stories or poetry.
- Writing (or talking into a tape recorder) for three minutes as a daily journal.
- Visualizing a scene of perfect calm, such as lying in a hammock or floating in a boat.
- Devoting time to prayer and reflection.

5. ADDers of all ages are notorious for falling asleep fully-dressed, a practice which should be discouraged for anyone having sleep problems. Many develop the habit because they have become accustomed to "crashing" after a cycle of high activity, but wearing street clothes to bed may actually hinder the sleeper's ability to enter "deep sleep." As long as the body is "dressed for action," the mind receives a cue for vigilance, and the quality of mental rest suffers.

Of course, we're not suggesting a pair of "Dr. Denton's" pajamas with the feet sewn in them or an old-fashioned

ADDers often fall asleep fully clothed.

nightshirt. In fact, some ADD youngsters may prefer sleeping in a t-shirt and shorts or sweats; this type of clothing is comfortable for many ADDers. The key is to designate an outfit which will be used **only** for sleeping. When the student dons the sleep outfit, it signals, "Time to relax."

Sleeping in street clothes and with the TV on is not quality sleep.

6. Another ADD problem area involves falling asleep in front of the television. Adult ADDers may recall the days of being prompted to head for their pillows by the playing of the national anthem when stations signed off the air. As one of our older clients once said, "To this day, when I hear the opening words 'O, say can you see...' I start yawning!"

Again, such sleep is deceptive, for the ears and mind remain tuned to the sensory input. This situation is illustrated by people who hear "real" telephones ring while asleep and consequently dream about picking up the receiver and having a conversation. Those who believe they "can't fall asleep without having the TV on" are kidding themselves because they never really get to sleep–particularly in an age when television stations never "sign off" the air.

Some die-hard "TV sleepers" have acquired televisions with sleep timers which will automatically shut off the machine after a certain number of minutes and have successfully "weaned" themselves from the habit. However, we suggest parents establish a nightly "no TV" time deadline for the entire household; all video entertainments must be turned off fifteen to thirty minutes before bedtime.

Should My ADD Child Try Therapeutic Medications?

Although medications have been used to treat ADD symptoms for over thirty years with great success, they have recently become a "lightning rod" of controversy in the media storm of attention surrounding Attention Deficit Disorder. This attention has intensified interest in ADD, but at times it has also brought "more heat than light" to discussions of the condition, tending to obscure an already confusing subject.

ADD and Medication

Scientific research has helped us understand the biological and chemical basis for ADD and how the actions of certain medications can improve the ADDers ability to concentrate and control impulses, but there is also a great deal left to learn about the nature of brain chemistry and its impact on human behaviors. The most basic medical question reflects the complexity of the condition itself: "Should medications be used in the treatment for ADD?" The only truthful response is: "Maybe yes, maybe no."

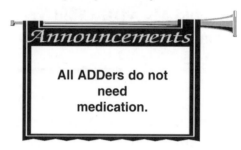

All ADDers do not need medication.

There are many "levels of involvement" in terms of ADD symptoms, and depending on a person's situation, medication may or may not be warranted. In fact, some of our ADD clients at Brainworks learn coping skills and/or practice behavioral strategies which successfully address their areas of greatest need; such people can successfully manage ADD without medication. However, other ADDers have a higher level of involvement with ADD, and medication provides them with the essential means of control so they are able to work on coping skills. For these ADDers, medication makes the difference between being able to perform at their maximum level of capability or being unable to function at all.

Between these two poles of experience are other levels of medication use. Some ADDers can function at a minimal level without medication, but they become capable of extraordinary achievements when medicated regularly. Others find they do not need medication every day, but they may resort to it on an "as needed" basis for tasks requiring sustained concentration. Still others do not use medication when they need to think creatively; the wide-ranging, free-associative thinking which comes naturally to the ADD mind best suits imaginative planning. Yet, these same ADD individuals may need medication in order to bring their plans into fruition.

Therefore, medication remains an intensely "individual" matter, and the decision to try medication should be based upon a thorough examination of the ADDer's specific situation. The only "hard and fast rule" about the issue is: **There is no hard and fast rule which applies universally.** At the Brainworks center, we are neither "pro" nor "con" concerning medication use, but we do believe that much of the current controversy about the topic could be resolved with the use of a little common sense and a lot of careful evaluation. **It is as erroneous to say everyone with ADD should be taking medication as it to say that no one with ADD should take medication.** The truth about medicine is that it is only a tool, and a tool is only useful if we know how to use it properly. The following tips offer guidelines for dealing with several key aspects of medication therapy.

1. When a child starts medication therapy, the parents and the prescribing doctor should spend time with the ADDer explaining why the medicine is being tried and what the student should expect from it. Some of the clients we see at Brainworks have absolutely no idea why they periodically take these pills or what the pills are supposed to do. It's hard for these individuals to supply much feedback information because they don't know what they are supposed to be noticing.

2. Once the decision to try medication is made, other questions arise: "What medication should the child take? How large should the dose be? How often should it be taken?" For some ADDers, finding the right medicine and dosage is a simple process; for others, the procedure will involve much "trial and error" before finding the right medicine (or combination of medicines).

The most crucial aspect of beginning medication is to **monitor the effects closely**. This monitoring should consist of self-observations by the ADDer and evaluations from various people who have contact with the student throughout the day, such as family members, teachers, and coaches.

Monitor medication closely.

Monitoring can take the form of a daily (sometimes hourly) checklist or a diary for an older person; but when eliciting feedback from young children, parents should ask specific questions to determine if the child has noticed any differences. For example, the parent could ask, "Did you have any arguments today in school? Did you write down the page numbers for your homework assignment? Did you lose track of your books or coat today?"

When asking teachers for feedback, the simple structure of primary grade classrooms can be an asset. Since the younger child spends most of the school day in one room with one teacher, there is a greater opportunity for that instructor to note the effects of medication trials. In higher grades, it will be necessary to get feedback from several teachers; this information can be valuable when checking the timing of medicine versus the demands placed on the student. For example, a student whose morning schedule consists of "high interest" classes such as art or choir may have few concentration problems at the start of the day, but the pattern may change after lunch when he must focus on subjects such as math or chemistry. (See Appendix for sample medication feedback forms.)

Individual responses to ADD medication vary widely; there does not seem to be an

absolute "standard dose" for people based on age or weight. Specific questions can help track the effects of the medication, information which is essential for the prescribing physician who needs to know whether to adjust the child's dosage or not. Without feedback from a variety of people who see the child "in action" every day, the doctor's ability to make decisions about medication is severely hindered. Unfortunately, this sort of "feedback" scenario is one which some people view with uncertainty. A doctor once asked the parent of one of our clients, "Is the medication working?" Her response was, "You're the doctor. Can't you tell?"

In order to monitor effectively, parents should learn how to talk to their doctor about ADD issues. For this reason, parents need to (a) be familiar with both the positive and negative effects of the medicine, (b) document the reaction(s) of the child, and (c) pass this information to the doctor on a regular basis.

The staff of Brainworks is often called upon to provide monitoring data for evaluating the effectiveness of medication, and our program includes a number of activities designed to test attention span, impulse reactions, and so forth. We closely observe our client's performances, both on and off medication, documenting any differences we may be able to detect.

One of the "bottom line" issues we face involves the emotional impact of medication. If the client shows improvement in task performance but simultaneously undergoes a negative change in terms of personality, we feel the medication therapy should be reviewed. For example, if a child

Call the doctor if the child's personality worsens.

who previously was energetic, vivacious, and sociable becomes lethargic, morose, and withdrawn when medicated, the therapy isn't truly "working" even if the child's grades improve. The ideal medicinal therapy will give the child control of focus without drastically altering the youngster's basic nature.

3. Parents and others who monitor medication effects should be aware of the impact timing can have on medication effectiveness. In other words, it's not just a matter of what kind of medicine and how large the dose is, it's also a matter of **when** the student takes the medicine. Again, individual reactions vary widely. Some ADDers need a larger dose in the morning than they do in the evening, while others may need a relatively small dose in the morning and a larger dose in

order to sit down and finish homework at night. In terms of timing, monitoring should answer these questions:

● How long does it seem to take for the medicine to "take affect" after the child swallows the pill?

● How long does the effect of the medicine last?

● At certain times of the day, is the dosage too high or too low? This determination can be made by noting how much effort and struggle is involved for the child to do similar tasks which require concentration at different times of the day. When "testing" an ADDer's concentration, parents should make sure the task presents a challenge to the student's attention span. For example, playing a video game would not be an appropriate test, for most ADDers can easily focus on a game with high interest components of flashing lights, bizarre sounds, and immediate feedback. A better evaluation can be obtained by monitoring the student's performance on homework or tedious chores.

4. When monitoring medication for adolescents, parents must be especially cautious about asking specific questions. Teenagers often have a difficult time accepting the need for medication.

Adolescence, in general, intensifies most of life's experiences, and the mix of "normal" adolescent behavior with ADD symptoms can be a recipe for personal disaster. Even those ADD teens who may have successfully

Recipe For Personal Disaster:
1. **Adolescence**
2. **ADD Symptoms**

taken medication since childhood may "rebel" against the schedule as a means of asserting independence, or they may reject taking the medicine because they are embarrassed about going to the nurse's office in front of their peers.

An additional problem comes from the fact that adolescents thrive on impulse and are attracted to stimulation. A medication which lowers one's impulsivity, increases concentration, and reduces distractions probably doesn't seem very attractive to the average teenager; most lively, fun-seeking sixteen year olds will not be too thrilled about taking a pill which encourages them to "buckle down" and get their homework done!

Adjusting to medication can be even more challenging for this age group if their ADD is diagnosed during the teen years. Adolescents may reject the diagnosis because it threatens their developing identity. They fear being labeled as

Some teenage ADDers reject the diagnosis of ADD.

"diseased," and they may deny the negative impact ADD is having on their lives in favor of blaming other people or "bad luck" for the problems they have.

Often, our clients describe the medication's effect as making them feel "weird." Such a response requires investigation, however. We have learned the word "weird" often refers to the fact that they are unfamiliar with the sensation of being focused and in control. One teenage client said the medicine made him feel "unhappy" in his biology class; on further questioning, we discovered his definition for being "happy" meant talking and joking with the students sitting around him for the entire class period. "Unhappy" translated as listening to the teacher and taking notes! (Indeed, the ADD teen who has developed the protective image of "class clown" may view medication as a plot to turn him into a "nerd.")

More than any other age group, teenagers may need professional guidance in order to benefit from their medication. In the end, learning to control the negative aspects of ADD will bring the result that every teen seeks: greater independence and personal success.

ADD is treated,
NOT cured.

5. As we move toward a better understanding of the role of medication in ADD therapy, **we must adjust our view of medicine from being a "cure" to being a "treatment."** Our society has become accustomed to the idea that we take pills until the problem "goes away," at which point the medicine is discontinued. Unfortunately, ADD medication doesn't follow this scenario, as some of our clients have learned the hard way.

The typical pattern for this "lesson" begins with an analysis of the severity of the student's ADD problems, an analysis indicating that for this ADD individual, medication is indicated as part of the management plan. After establishing the best dosage schedule, the student seems to have a "miraculous" turnaround in terms of grades and behavior, and the ADDer begins to experience success both in and out of the classroom. However, a month or so later, the "miracle" begins to unravel; low grades and "missing" homework assignments recur, followed by a crash of self-esteem and behavioral problems. When parents turn to our center for an explanation, we have learned to ask a crucial first question: "Is the child taking his medication on the same schedule?" Quite often, the answer we receive is, "Well, we stopped giving him the medicine. He didn't need it anymore!"

These parents have seen the improvement in the child's performance as proof of a "cure," and when the medicine is withdrawn and the negative behaviors return, they may see it as a "relapse." Of course, the truth is that **there is no cure for ADD**, as much as we might wish it so. Medication provides the ADDer with a "handle" to guide actions and help with decisions, but it is not a "permanent fix."

For some ADDers, medication may possibly be a "lifetime" strategy, although we have read about more and more case studies which suggest some ADDers may be able to "wean themselves" from medication over long periods of time through establishing structures, training concentration spans, and employing behavioral modification. These stories are encouraging for ADDers who find the concept of "medication for life" repellent, but we must also recognize the dangers inherent in abruptly discontinuing medication. Not only will doing so have a physical effect on the child, it may also be psychologically damaging for a student who has begun to regain self-esteem based upon his improved performance; the sudden return of the original problems can shatter the child's feelings of new-found hope and confidence.

Once a child has started therapeutic medication, the schedule should not be abandoned without consulting the prescribing doctor. Furthermore, if the decision is made to stop medication, the child should be prepared to expect the changes which will occur.

Consult Your Doctor.

INTRODUCTION

Behavior Issues

First of all, we need to be clear about what the word "motivation" implies. Frequently, parents will tell us, "My son isn't motivated to clean his room," or "My daughter needs to be more motivated about getting her homework finished." These situations have more to do with establishing **structured expectations and consequences** than with motivation. For example, most adults don't pay their utility bills every month because they are "motivated" to do so; they do it because failing to pay results in a negative consequence—such as having the electricity turned off! This cause and effect dynamic shapes many of our everyday behaviors, and though we may believe we are making "choices" or "being motivated," to perform certain tasks, in reality we are simply responding to structures. However, motivation can exert a powerful influence on a person's actions, an influence which can take either a positive or negative path.

**Positive
Motivation –
Self-esteem put
into action.**

A dictionary definition of "motive" tells us the word pertains to a "desire or inspiration which incites action," a description which doesn't necessarily mean only "good actions." At Brainworks, we view **positive motivation as self-esteem put into action**. Positively motivated students get enthused about learning, and they see school as a positive proving ground for their talents. These students get to school on time—not because there is a consequence for being tardy, but because they are inspired by what goes on in their classrooms. They desire to be part of an environment where they feel accepted and successful.

On the other hand, if students see school as a place which confirms their feelings of failure, their greatest "desire" may be to avoid the classroom. Such students are, indeed, motivated to take action, although the action may take the form of tardies and/or "skipping" school. Unfortunately, the behaviors of far too many ADD teenagers fall into this "negative motivation" category.

What Can Help "Motivate" An ADD Teenager?

By the time many of our adolescent ADD clients come to our center, they have developed a bitter and cynical outlook toward life. Some have begun to hate themselves, and they may be self-destructive in their behaviors. Our challenge is to convert the "negativity" of these young adults into a positive force, helping them regain a sense of hope and a belief in their own abilities. The following suggestions have helped "motivate" many of our clients in the right directions.

1. The word **"lazy"** must be eliminated from the vocabulary of parents, teachers, and the

ADD teenager, an elimination which requires changing not only semantics, but also point of view. Calling someone "lazy" presumes the individual makes a **conscious choice** to avoid doing something; however, with ADDers, there is not a choice so much as there is a "reflex."

> **–ADD–**
> **It's NOT an issue of morality;**
> **it is an issue of biology.**

When presented with a task or materials they perceive as uninteresting or incomprehensible, the brains of ADDers literally "turn off." The brain chemicals (neurotransmitters) necessary to maintain focus and attention may not "flow" consistently, so ADD minds **automatically** switch to ideas which do stimulate the brain chemistry— ideas which, unfortunately, may not be in their third period teacher's lesson plans. No matter how hard the ADD student may try and no matter how many tortured hours may be spent staring at the assignment, he cannot "force" himself to do it through sheer will power. **It is not an issue of morality; it is an issue of biology.**

When an adult calls an ADD student "lazy," the comment will not "motivate" the student to perform, but it may damage the quality of their relationship and lower the ADDer's self-esteem.

ADDers should be expected to meet commitments and respond to obligations, but their special struggles should be recognized and understood. Instead of saying the student is "lazy," adults should acknowledge the challenges of ADD, assist in designing coping strategies, and offer words of positive encouragement for efforts made in addressing problems.

2. Have the ADD teenager make two lists, one labeled "Permanent Assets" and the other designated "Temporary Deficiencies." Under the "Assets" heading, the student should list his positive attributes and gifts; the list might include qualities such as creativity, loyalty to friends, sense of humor, originality, and so forth. In the "Deficiencies" column, the student should list his negative areas which need to be improved, such as getting to class on time, test grades in Spanish, or relationships with family members. Most ADDers find it far easier to list their faults than their strengths, having heard "what's wrong with them" from numerous sources throughout their

Permanent Assets	Temporary Deficiencies
_____	_____
_____	_____
_____	_____

lives; however, they may need help coming up with a list of their positive qualities.

After making these lists, the ADDer and the "adult advisor" should review the items noted and discuss possible strategies for using the assets to remediate the deficiencies. An example of such a strategic plan might be to employ the "loyalty to friends" trait to improve "test grades in Spanish" by arranging to meet a classmate for a "study buddy" review session prior to major tests. A single commitment made to a friend is usually taken far more seriously by an ADDer than a million promises and pledges made to himself.

ADDers need visual reminders of their goals to keep them motivated.

3. Visual cues can have an impact on ADD motivation and behavior. When working on a long-term goal, the ADD student should try placing Post-it® notes in strategic spots as "big picture" reminders. For example, one of our brightest sixteen year old ADD clients had a powerful desire to attend Duke University; but in order to

achieve this ambitious goal, he needed to improve his grades immediately and maintain this improvement over the "long haul" of his last two years of high school. To keep himself "inspired," he put Post-it® reminders with the word DUKE written on them in several places, including on his bathroom mirror, above his desk, and inside the door of his school locker. Another client decorated her room with pennants and posters from her "dream college." (NOTE: Such reminders should be written and placed by the ADD students themselves.)

4. Low self-esteem is one of the most tragic side effects of unmanaged ADD symptoms, but we have seen dramatic improvements in our clients' self-images when they spend time reviewing information about Attention Deficit Disorder. Learning about the condition helps them understand their frustrations and reactions; they discover that although they may have special problems, they also have special gifts. They find comfort in the fact they're "not alone," and that other ADDers deal with many of the same issues they do. Most importantly, they change their views of themselves from the negative to the positive.

ADD education builds self-esteem.

Talk to other ADDers.

We present ADD information in an "ADD friendly" format by presenting videos, newsletters, brief excerpts from books and articles, and "mini-autobiographies" written by other ADD teenagers as sources of information. We encourage them to talk to other ADDers (adults as well as teenage peers) about the "joys and pain" of ADD experiences. Spending as little as 15 to 30 minutes per week on ADD education can make a lifetime's worth of difference in terms of self-esteem.

5. Some ADD teens quickly disconnect from high school classes they perceive as being "pointless" or "useless" because they operate on the basis of satisfying "immediate needs" only. Their lack of foresight makes it extremely difficult for them to focus on "long-range" prospects; some ADD teens don't think far enough ahead to plan for next weekend, much less know what they want to do with the rest of their lives. (We once asked an ADD high school senior, "What do you plan to do after you graduate?" His reply was, "I think we're going to have a party at the lake.")

However, **many experts believe establishing an "ADD friendly" career direction has an enormous impact on the ADD student's ability to achieve**. First of all, choosing such a career path stimulates the ADDer's thinking processes in general, and if the student gets "excited" by the idea of being a zoologist or becoming a pilot, the energy derived from this excitement will "infect" the youngster's overall attitude. Also, the day-to-day activities in the student's classes will have some concrete relevance; the student needs to take his math homework seriously because pilots must be able to work out navigational computations or because zoology degrees require several semesters of upper-level math classes.

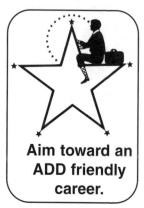

Aim toward an ADD friendly career.

Investigate Career Options

Parents and teachers can encourage ADDers to explore and investigate possible career options in several "active" ways. The ADDer can interview a person who works in the field which interests them, or spend a day visiting a college department or a training school; some teachers assign such investigations and interviews as research project assignments, an excellent way to prompt students into thinking of career paths.

Students with a high level of interest in certain occupations may even be eligible to work as part-time "interns" during summers or weekends in that field. For example, a student interested in journalism might work part-time for the local newspaper or television news staff. It may turn out that the "internship" experience makes them realize this sort of job doesn't interest them after all. However, the situation won't be entirely negative, because they will have saved a lot of time and energy pursuing a career which wasn't right for them in the first place!

SAMPLE "ADD FRIENDLY" CAREERS

Law enforcement officer/detective
Journalist
Television/ radio broadcasting
Advertising/public relations
Military (combat personnel)
Architecture/interior design
Emergency services (paramedic, firefighter)
Salesperson/stock broker
Wilderness guide/forest ranger
Medicine (surgery, emergency room)
Law (criminal law, litigation)

A list of "ADD friendly" careers can be as diverse as the interests of ADDers themselves. For instance, some ADD students love working with computers and may be highly motivated about learning to design and develop creative software programs. Other ADD students loathe dealing with technology of any kind, but they possess highly developed "people skills" and would make excellent counselors or therapists. Still other ADDers may apply their verbal or artistic abilities to the field of advertising. The key elements are the individual's ability to (a) get excited about the work and (b) have some form of "variety" in their tasks. On the other hand, jobs which bore the ADDer or which focus on following highly structured routines tend to be poor employment choices.

How Can ADD Teenagers Improve Their Social Skills?

One of the most important components of the Brainworks' program is our use of peer-age tutors in one-on-one contacts with clients. While most teens will "turn off" their attention when adults start "lecturing them" about school or behavior issues, the youngsters tend to be more responsive if the ideas are presented by someone

closer to their age. Our tutors, recruited from the ranks of high school "gifted and talented" classes in our area, provide positive personal reinforcement for our teenage ADD clients as they

ADDers listen to peers. address areas such as communication skills, decision-making, and mood management. In addition, our tutors serve as "successful student role models" for ADDers; the tutors frequently share their own "survival tips" concerning classes, tests, or assignments with the clients.

Certainly, peer tutors are essential elements in our social skill activities. Many ADDers have problems maintaining friendships and coping with "peer group dynamics," problems which may lead eventually to feelings of rejection and alienation. Why do relationships present such difficulties for ADDers? Some classic ADD characteristics (impatience, impulsivity, nonconformity, restlessness, and lack of self-observation) can probably be blamed; the intensity of "the ADD personality" can be very hard on friends and family.

ADD Relationship Obstacles
- Impatience
- Impulsivity
- Nonconformity
- Restlessness
- Lack of self-observation
- Intensity of personality

For example, the ADDer's problems with maintaining a consistent attention span has a tremendous impact on relationships. ADDers have been described as being "distracted" because their attention shifts uncontrollably to sights and sounds of the world around them. This behavior has been labeled as representing an "attention deficit," a term which may have come from people annoyed when ADDers turned to watch traffic flow outside the window rather than listen to what the non-ADDers were saying. The logic behind the label is clear enough: "What I'm saying is terribly important, and if you can't pay attention—well, then you have a disorder of some kind which makes you unable to pay attention to what's important—such as ME!"

All kidding aside, **the term "attention deficit" is an inaccurate one**. ADDers don't have a lack of attention; in fact, they have exactly the opposite problem, which is an **over-abundance of attention**. The problems they have are related to the fact that they have no control over their attention. Consequently, carrying on a dialogue with an ADDer can be an exercise in frustration. Throughout the conversation, the ADD mind drifts in and out, frequently misinterpreting messages, interrupting the other person, and switching to new topics; such behaviors do not encourage the meaningful communication which forms the basis of friendship.

ADD:

An Over Abundance

Of Attention

The irony lies in the fact that despite an often carefully cultivated "lone wolf" image, ADDers truly need the guidance and perspective provided by loyal advisors and the motivation of "emotional cheerleaders" to help them stay on task and maintain optimism. Without a foundation of positive peer relationships, the life of an ADD student can become a miserable and solitary existence.

On the other hand, ADDers can also be "the best of best friends" to have. Their generosity, enthusiasm, and sincerity combined with their creative gifts and spontaneous humor makes for fun and exciting companionship. The following guidelines will help "lay the groundwork" for ADDers to develop positive and lasting relationships.

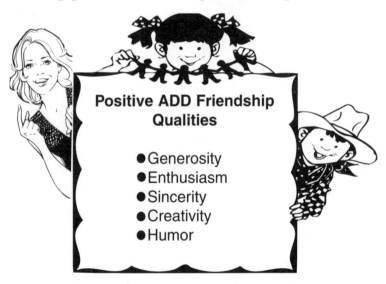

Positive ADD Friendship Qualities

- Generosity
- Enthusiasm
- Sincerity
- Creativity
- Humor

1. A key element for ADDers seeking to improve their social skills is to increase their self-awareness. To this end, the Brainworks staff employs a variety of personal evaluation checklists. Such inventories can be obtained from a variety of sources, including magazines, self-help workbooks, and counseling centers; occasionally, our staff will create a checklist to meet a particular need.

Social Skills

Checklist

These checklists provide a structure for self-analysis and serve as a springboard for "follow-up" discussions between the student and tutor about different personality types. For instance, after students work through a checklist designed to evaluate whether the subject is an introvert or an extrovert, they may end up talking about what it would be like to go on a camping trip with a group of introverts versus a group of extroverts.

The checklists we use assess a myriad of qualities, including "right and left brain" hemisphere dominance, learning styles, temperament, stress factors, and so on. These lists have a high interest appeal for ADD students because they are presented in a non-threatening manner, with no "right or wrong" answers and because they work on them in tandem with their teenage tutors. At the end of each session, both of them have to compose brief statements concerning what they have learned about themselves and about their partner as a result of the exercise.

2. Chatting with ADDers sometimes tends to become "competition conversing" because they don't "take turns" when speaking with others. Their impatience to get their message across causes them to interrupt their partners and to fail to listen carefully enough to get the full message. One way to overcome this tendency is to have "conversation games" between three people.

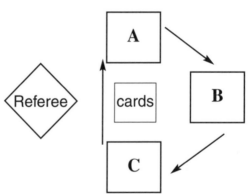

The game requires a box full of discussion topics, three players, and a "referee" to monitor whether the players "stick to the subject" and listen to the other members of the group. In order to speak, a person has to be holding a item, such as an index card; no one in the game is allowed to speak without holding the card. The first speaker draws a "personal opinion" topic ("what kind of music I like best"), and he talks about the topic for approximately one minute.

The card is then passed to the second "player" who must then (a) summarize what the first speaker said and (b) spend a minute expressing her opinion on the same topic. The card is next passed to the third person who summarizes the position of the first two players and offers one minute of opinion. When the third player hands the card back to the first player, the speaker summarizes the opinions of players two and three, and then passes the topic choices to player two, who draws a new topic and begins the next cycle.

If a player fails to offer a satisfactory summation of the others' opinions or gets off the subject, the "referee" assesses foul points, the object being to have as low a score as possible. When we have played this game at Brainworks, we have seen definite improvement in our ADD clients' ability to follow the rhythm of normal conversations, an ability that transfers to their conversations at home and at school.

3. ADD teenagers have an especially difficult time dealing with non-verbal communication issues.   This difficulty is evident in their inability to "read the body language" of other people; it is

also seen in the teen's lack of awareness of what non-verbal messages they send to others through voice tone, posture, and facial expressions. Confusion regarding non-verbal communication often leads to a great deal of unnecessary personal conflict and turmoil in the lives of ADD teens.

ADDers often ignore body language cues.

Another Brainworks publication, **Teenage Connection**, devotes a special section to exercises designed to improve a teenager's awareness of how non-verbal factors can alter communication. For example, one activity gives teenagers a series of common remarks:

> *"Where did you get that shirt?"*
> *"I noticed your test grade."*
> *"Did you really want to win?"*
> *"How could you?"*
> *"You blew it!"*
> *"Too bad."*

The teenagers then sit "back to back" and practice saying each statement using different tones of voice, including sarcastic, enthusiastic, sympathetic, and whiny. They then analyze how each message would be received differently by the listener and how the listener might respond to the tone of voice cues. Eventually, the teen comes to see that a message isn't just the words being said, but how they are said. For example, the comments of ADDers often sound more sarcastic than they are meant to be.

Freaked out!

Our clients also evaluate the impact of posture and actions on communication. In another **Teenage Connection** activity, the students are given a list of emotional expressions (Joy, "Cool," Humor, Fear, Depression, Boredom, and Anger). The student chooses one and then pantomimes the emotion for the partner. The partner observes the actions of the performing teen and tries to "guess" which emotion is being portrayed. Then they swap roles and the partner must choose an emotion to "act out." This exercise is particularly helpful to illustrate for the teen why teachers are offended by body language which indicates "boredom."

Yet another exercise focuses on meanings which can be conveyed by eye contact. This time, the two students use sheets of paper to cover their faces—except for their eyes. They take turns trying to communicate messages such as "apologizing," "teasing," "pleading innocent," "lying," "hero worshipping," "getting caught," and "acting pleased." The activity makes ADD teens more conscious of how they handle "eye contact" in their own conversations. (One client even reported he realized the "eye expressions" he used with his boss may have cost him a job!)

 Eyes can convey a message.

4. One of the best exercises in **Teenage Connection** presents twelve "face only" pictures of various teenagers taken from eight photographs; the pictures present a wide variety of expressions. The client must decide which pictures represent people who would not be talking to each other; the next task is to identify the emotion portrayed in each photo and to guess what could have happened to provoke the expression, and the final phase is to attempt to guess which pictures could be "photo partners." The student must explain the reasons for his guesses, and the activity ends with a series of questions designed to help the student understand the "how and why" behind the guesses and interpretations.

5. Technology can improve communication skills. We have used tape recorders to help ADDers review their "tone of voice" messages and videotapes of "practice" job and scholarship interviews which can also increase the ADDer's awareness of non-verbal messages.

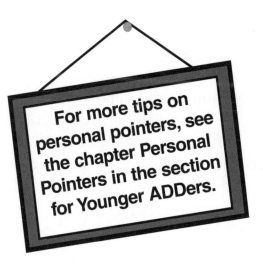

For more tips on personal pointers, see the chapter Personal Pointers in the section for Younger ADDers.

Part Two

Quick Tips for Younger ADDers

—1

TIME AND SPACE

INTRODUCTION

 How Can The Clutter And Confusion In An ADD Child's Life Be Reduced?

 How Can An ADD Child Learn Time Management?

 Why Is It So Difficult To Get An ADD Child Ready For School In The Morning?

INTRODUCTION

Time and Space Issues

Most young children, whether they have ADD or not, are not especially concerned with organization or time management issues. However, non-ADD children seem to incorporate structure into their lives as they mature much more easily than ADD children; in addition, children without ADD have an innate "time sense" which ADD children do not possess.

For the ADD child, organization and time awareness are skills which will never be "natural" or "automatic." He will probably have to employ a variety of external structures to organize himself and keep himself aware of time. The parent who expects an ADD child to "out-grow" problems with time and organization will have a long and disappointing wait ahead.

Unfortunately, some parents deal with their children's time and space problems by taking on the role of "rescuer." The parent assumes the responsibility for keeping the child on schedule, tracking school assignments, dealing with teachers, organizing notebooks, putting away toys, and so on. This tactic is detrimental in two ways. First, rescuing prevents the child from developing the skills which allow him to function independently; eventually, this dependence creates feelings of helplessness because the ADDer never learns the problem-solving skills he will need to survive on his own.

The second negative impact of rescuing involves the relationship between the rescuer and the child. What the rescuer perceives as a "help-

ing hand" may be resented by the person being helped. Most ADDers are fiercely independent souls who become agitated by "interference" from authority figures. In the end, the rescuer feels unappreciated while the student

Rescued ADDer. seethes with anger and frustration.

Of course, parents have a natural protective instinct regarding their children, and many times their assistance can provide ADD children with a chance to learn how to handle problems. However, parents need to monitor carefully both the depth and frequency of the aid they are rendering in order to avoid handicapping the development of their children.

A better approach is to introduce the ADD

child to the concept of using external structures as early as possible and to present these strategies in a positive manner. Some strategies may even seem like "games" to a youngster, and due to the child's more open and adaptable nature, there will be less resistance to introducing structures at this age than in adolescent years. By establishing some basic routines and trying some coping "tricks," a parent will not only reduce the child's level of stress, but he will also develop her confidence and sense of independence–an excellent foundation for both academic achievement and personal progress.

The first step in presenting a coping tip to the child involves convincing the child of the need to try the tip. **The usual ADD reaction to a problem situation is a combination of denial and wishful thinking.** The denial comes in the form of seeing each problem as a unique situation

Teacher's fault	Bad Luck	Sloppy work
Procrastination		Next time will be different
Parent's fault	Not in the mood	I'll just remember

ADD Denial And Wishful Thinking

based on external factors, not as part of an ADD-based pattern of behavior. Rather than face the reality of his ADD tendencies, the child may blame other people or "bad luck" for the problem; in some cases, he may even convince himself that his "sloppiness" and procrastination are a matter of choice, not a result of ADD symptoms. Once this denial is in place, the next phase is wishful thinking, "Next time it will be different."

In order to overcome these mental obstacles, parents must document the problem in writing for the child. For example, if the child fails a test because he forgot to bring a book home, ask the child exactly what happened, why it happened, how he will prevent it from happening again, and record this information. When the child responds with, "Next time I'll just remember my book," write this statement on the sheet. When the problem recurs, show the paper to the child as proof that his method did not work, that this incident is part of an ongoing pattern, and that he needs a tip to help him remember.

Problem-Solving Questions

1. What specifically happened?
2. When did it happen?
3. Why did it happen?
4. How can you prevent it from happening again?

There are other crucial factors for parents to keep in mind as they work with their children on these tips. First of all, parents should **model the strategy** for the child. In other words, if the child is supposed to use a checklist for chores, the parent should also use a similar checklist for "grown-up" chores. This modeling presents the checklist as a "normal" activity which even adults use, and removes the possibility that the child will view it as a punishment for "being bad."

Moreover, a parent who models the tip learns to appreciate more fully what the child is going through as he works on the strategy. If a parent does not model a behavior, yet expects the child to assimilate the behavior, a conflict will eventually arise–and there will be no winners in this battle.

Finally, parents should examine the expectations they have for their ADD children. While external structures can make a huge difference in how ADDers manage certain aspects of their lives, these **"survival skills" will not alter the ADD thinking style, nor will they "cure" the condition.** It's a good idea to periodically review these guidelines:

1. Be aware of the child's peer group capabilities; communicate with other parents whose children are of the same age group about problems

and expectations. However, always keep in mind that in terms of emotional maturity, ADDers develop much more slowly than their non-ADD peers, at an approximate 30% delay. An ADD child 9 years old chronologically operates at the emotional level of a six year old. (This pattern of delayed development will be consistent through-out the life span of the ADDer.)

2. Don't confuse a child's high intelligence with organizational abilities.

3. Understand change does not occur in a vacuum; adjustments expected of the child will affect the entire family.

4. Realize consistency of effort will be the determining factor in the success of the tip.

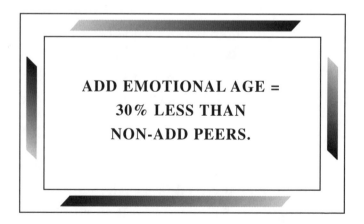

**ADD EMOTIONAL AGE =
30% LESS THAN
NON-ADD PEERS.**

How Can The Clutter And Confusion In An ADD Child's Life Be Reduced?

1. Limit the amount of furniture in the child's room to the necessary essentials–bed, dresser, lamp and storage bins. Most ADD children don't need a desk so much as they need a "distraction free zone" to do homework (see STUDY STRATEGIES in the section for the ADD Teens and Adults). Moreover, children, in general, seem to use their desks as nothing more than as glorified shelves; the little chairs accompanying the desks usually end up being makeshift hanging racks for jackets and sweaters.

However, open shelves and bookcases are useful pieces of furniture, especially if they are wide enough to hold bins and tubs.

Open shelves can hold bins and tubs for "stuff."

2. Use clear plastic bins or colored laundry baskets for storing and sorting toys and clothes. Make sure that the basket/bin for the child's dirty laundry is a distinctly different color from baskets/bins used for clean or stored clothes. (If clothes need to be stain-treated before washing, encourage the child to tie the item into a knot while undressing, or have a special dark-colored basket for stained items.)

3. Toy boxes which contain thousands of "action figures," building blocks, or any collection of "tiny pieces" should be lined with a sheet. The sheet can be gathered together, lifted out of the box, and spread out on the floor as a play area. When playtime is over, the child can re-gather the toys in the sheet and put everything away in one motion.

4. Obtain "under the bed" boxes and use them to store items which are not needed for periods of time, such as off-season clothes and shoes, toys, or school papers from past semesters.

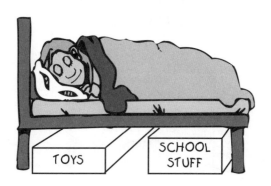

5. Make a "blueprint style" diagram for your child, marking the "proper places" the child is expected to put things when tidying the room. (Visual references are much more effective for ADDers than verbal instructions.)

6. Label the drawers, bins, and boxes where the child's clothes and toys are kept with both pictures of the items and written labels. These designations will reduce the amount of confusion and the number of decisions the child must make when putting things away.

7. Avoid giving general instructions to the child such as, "Clean your room." Instead, make out a checklist of specific chores for the child to follow. (See the Appendix for a sample checklist.) For every chore on the list, the child should estimate how long it will take for her to do the task, and then time how long the chore actually takes.

8. Encourage the child to make his own checklists when planning for trips, birthday parties, campouts, or any "fun" activity. Associating such lists with events which are entertaining for the child presents the strategy of checklists in a positive light, and when the child makes out his own checklists, it creates a greater sense of independence and self-control. He feels more "in charge."

9.` Every so often, allow the child to make a checklist for her parents to follow. For example, the child could make a checklist for what items the parent needs to carry to work, or one for assembling the child's lunchbox. Another good checklist for the child to work with is the weekly grocery list. Keep this shopping list posted in the kitchen. When the child wants a special lunch or snack item, it's her responsibility to add it to the list; if she doesn't put it on the list, then she shouldn't expect it to be purchased.

SUZAN'S
SHOPPING LIST

-raisins	-fun size candy
-string cheese	-fruit cups
-granola bars	-pudding cups
-cookies	-carrot sticks
-grape juice box	-lunch meat
-crackers	-peanut butter

Again, these strategies present checklists in a non-threatening way, and they may also provide the parent and child with an opportunity to discuss the importance of making plans.

10. Mnenomic devices such as acronyms help the child remember sequences of steps for chores or for school. Here's an acronym one parent created for the child to follow when tidying his room.

How To Clean Room

Put clothes in hamper
Empty trash can
Straighten bedspread
Toys in toy box

11. Most ADD children hate to "make the bed" because it's time-consuming and because within a few hours, the bed will be rumpled up again. From the child's point of view, it's a chore which is both tedious and useless. However, as many ADD adults have learned, spreading a comforter on the bed takes only a few seconds and creates the proper tidy appearance.

How Can An ADD Child Learn Time Management?

Certainly, we can't expect a young child to approach time management with the same degree of purpose which an adult might, but there are some strategies which can help even primary age children increase their awareness of time and the impact it has on their lives.

1. Work with the child on creating a basic **"week at a glance"** schedule which reflects his actual activities, making sure to plan for "free time" as well as chores and study time. (See the appendix for another sample schedule.)

January 13-15	16-19 January	
13 Monday	Thursday **16**	
14 Tuesday	Friday **17**	
15 Wednesday	Saturday **18**	Sunday **19**

It is crucial to present the idea of scheduling in a positive manner and not as a "punishment." ADDers in general often view schedules as prisons or as plots to destroy all their fun. One young ADD client at Brainworks reacted to a blank daily schedule sheet by saying, "Look at all those blanks! Now you're going to fill them up with stuff I don't want to do!"

A good way to present the daily schedule is to introduce it initially as a means of setting aside non-work or "goof-off" time. If the child wants to spend from 4:30-5:30 each day playing with friends, he should block out that time on his schedule; the parent should encourage him to keep the play time "appointment" as best he can. If something comes up to interfere with this plan, have the child note what happened on his schedule and talk with him about the need for plans to be flexible.

Other guidelines for the daily schedule include:

• On Sundays, sit with the child and her schedule and, using a television program guide, plan which shows the child will watch for the week. Have the child write these shows on her weekly schedule. An added advantage of

Schedule TV time.

this activity is it helps parents keep track of what kinds of television shows the child is watching and how much time is being spent on television.

• If a child procrastinates about starting a chore, time how long it takes him to begin and write this time on the schedule. Call the child's attention to this time and make it clear that his goal is to reduce the time it takes to start a chore. Reward the child when he makes progress toward reducing the time. (See Appendix for sample chore checklists.)

• Teach the child how to balance work time and play time in her schedule. ADDers tend to see time as an **"all or nothing"** proposition. In other words, they see life as being **all play or all work,** with nothing in between. This perspective partly accounts for their resistance to doing homework; having just spent eight hours "working" at school, they believe even one homework assignment robs them of the rest of the day!

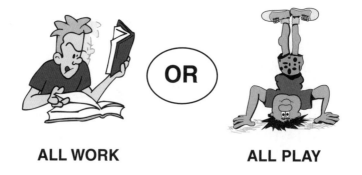

ALL WORK **ALL PLAY**

• In order to help the ADD child start to understand the concept of balancing work and play, translate the idea into a concrete visual reference. Color code the activities on the child's schedule, using one color for "homework/chore time" and another for "play/free time." The goal is to have both colors in proportional amounts for each day.

2. Make sure the child learns to tell time on an analog as well as a digital clock. There are distinct differences in how the two timepieces represent time. A digital clock offers time in a precise manner ("It's 11:54," as opposed to "nearly noon.") However, the

Digital Watch

digital also only offers time as **NOW**, without any frame of reference to time past or time ahead; all the child sees is a group of numbers.

On the other hand, an analog clock presents

Analog Watch

time in a completely different perspective; time is seen as motion through space instead of just a set of digits. The sweep of the second hand, the movement of the minute hand, and the cycle of hours on the face of the clock demonstrate both the pace and the scope of time. When we look at the face of an analog clock, we see a spatial representation of twelve hours, which puts the **NOW** moment in a context of past and future time. Also, analog clocks reinforce math skills, such as fractions ("It's a quarter past six.") and counting by fives, tens, etc.

Note: ADDers by nature usually operate primarily in the **NOW** mode most of the time; ADD experts point out for ADDers there are two types of time–**NOW** is one type and **"all other time"** is the other. For this reason, digital wristwatches may be a poor choice for ADD children and adults.

3. Encourage the child to wear a wristwatch (see the Note above). However, don't spend a great deal of money getting an expensive
watch because when
the child loses it (and
it's almost a certainty that
he will!), the result will be
a lot of unnecessary guilt,
anger, and recrimination. In
addition, stay away from "state of the
art" models with a dozen or so functions; such a timepiece will be so complicated that the child will seldom look at it. Instead, buy several simple,

ADDers like novelty watches.

inexpensive "fun" watches with colors, cartoon characters, or other eye-attracting designs. (A watch with a "stopwatch" function can be useful for timing tasks.)

Allowing the child to have input in choosing the watch will lower resistance to wearing it. Be sure the child tries on the watch before making the purchase. ADDers are notoriously sensitive about physical comfort issues, and some of them simply can't wear tight metal watchbands. They often prefer cloth or leather straps worn loosely on the arm.

4. On the child's daily schedule, draw a small picture of an analog clock with the hands corresponding to the time of each chore/activity next to the planned activity. (The digital time can be written under the clock picture.)

Exercise dog at 4:30

5. Use "day of the week" pill dispensers if the child is taking ADD medicine to increase awareness of time and to help him understand the pattern of his medication schedule.

6. During lengthy family driving trips, give the child a photocopy of the travel map and let her "plot the course" the trip is taking. Have her estimate the time it will take to drive from one town/city to the next. (This activity also helps the child develop map skills as well as increase time awareness.)

Why Is It So Difficult To Get An ADD Child Ready For School In The Morning?

Most ADDers (and a sizeable number of non-ADDers!) have problems getting their "engines going" in the morning. One reason behind this struggle is the almost universal difficulty ADDers have with sleep patterns. Some may be unable to fall asleep for hours; others may fall asleep easily only to wake up at 3:00 a.m. and be unable to go back to sleep. Therefore, the first issue the parent of an ADD child might consider when the child appears sleepy is whether or not the child is getting both the proper quality and quantity of sleep. If the child has serious sleep problems, check with his physician. (See PERSONAL POINTERS for ADD Teens and Adults.)

However, another issue with "getting ready for school" involves time awareness and structure–two areas with which ADDers often have problems. An ADD child can be mentally distracted and "drift away" while getting dressed; he ends up spending fifteen minutes putting on one pair of socks. Or, a child may be unaware how long it takes to get dressed, so he puts off the task until he is running late without even realizing it. Still another child may be unable to decide whether to get dressed or pack his backpack first, and he spends all his time trying to make up his mind.

Many parents of ADD children are also familiar with the routine of "the last minute frenzy." This panic occurs when the child is rushing to get ready, is almost out the door, and then– "OOPS! I forgot that I'm supposed to bring (fill in-the-blank) for class today!" The child and the hapless parent run around madly for a few minutes, obtaining the necessary item(s). Then they race to school in time for the child to enter class in a whirlwind mood–late, of course.

The damage this "panic" causes to the nerves of all involved is obvious. However, the damage also extends to the child's classroom performance. When a child begins the school day in this manner described, it will take him a long time to "settle down" and get sorted out to start the day. In the end, it takes a toll on the child's ability to perform in class.

There are ways to help the "madcap mornings" of the ADD child become less stressful.

1. If a child has trouble waking up on his own, place **two or more alarm clocks** in the child's room. One should be next to the bed, but the one with the loudest alarm should be placed where the child must get up and walk across the room to switch it off . (One good spot is inside a closet hanging among the child's shirts; another good spot is in a nearby bathroom.)

Near the bed

Away from bed

2. Use fun and unusual clocks for the child's room, such as roaring dinosaur clocks or "talking clocks." Make sure the alarms are loud–even annoying. **DO NOT** use radio music or

"snooze button" alarm clocks. Most ADDers can sleep through the music on their favorite station because they're familiar with it and enjoy listening to it; the snooze button allows them a choice they should **not** be allowed.

3. Make a list of every step the child follows to get ready in the morning. For several days, use a stopwatch to time how long each task takes. (How long to brush teeth, to eat, to shower, etc.) Use these times to help the child determine why he must get up at the designated time. Record these times and post them in a visible spot so the child becomes more aware of how much time is being used.

Time how long the ADDer takes to shower.

4. If the television is on, the child can use the shows as cues for actions. For example, when the "Today" show starts, he should be getting dressed, or when "Bugs Bunny" is over, he should be finishing breakfast.

5. After completing homework at night, the child should go ahead and pack her book bag or backpack for the following day and place it next to the exit door. Clothes for the next day can be set aside the night before as well, barring adjustments for surprise weather situations.

6. Use **"the kitchen timer on the stove"** to cue children who take too long at a particular task, such as getting dressed. If fifteen minutes have been allotted for putting on clothes, set the timer to go off in 10 minutes. This first ring cues the child that only five minutes remain. Reset the timer for five more minutes. If he is dressed on time, reward with praise. If he's not ready on the second ring, collect the clothes and the child, put them in the car, and have the child dress on the way to school! (Note: This "last resort" strategy has been tried by several parents of our younger clients, and these parents have discovered they only have to do it once!)

The stove timer helps schedule the ADDer.

For additional tips on organization and time issues, see chapters Organization Options and Time Tips in the section for teenagers and adults.

STUDY STRATEGIES

INTRODUCTION

 How Does ADD Affect Reading Ability?

 How Does ADD Affect Math Ability?

 How Does ADD Affect Writing Skills?

Introduction

 What Physical Factors Affect The Handwriting Of The ADD Child?

 What Role Does Memory Play In Handwriting Skills Of The ADD Child?

 What Can Improve The Composition Skills of ADD Students?

INTRODUCTION

Study Strategies

Despite the generally high intelligence levels of ADDers, academic achievement usually does not come easily for them. In fact, ADD is often undetected until a child begins having problems with formal schooling.

Prior to entering school, the ADD child has probably lived with relatively simple structures and few demands; the world consists of the family structure and the familiar territory of home. Upon entering elementary school, this child travels to a radically new environment, one of crowds, noise, conformity, and specific expectations.

The same child who in kindergarten was praised as "inventive" is now chastised for being "off task." Comments and behaviors previously considered amusing, original, and precocious are now characterized as disruptive or clownish. Instruction and assignments may emphasize rote memorization and repetitious production, and "good behavior" might be defined as the ability to sit quietly in a plastic chair for extended periods of time while concentrating with rapt attention to the spoken words of the teacher. If the child is distracted by noises outside the window or insists on drawing pictures of dancing robots instead of coloring within the lines, points may be deducted from the child's "citizenship" grade.

This description may sound harsh (as indeed it is), but it also reflects the emotional perspective of many overwhelmed little ADDers. Given the unintentionally "hostile" nature of this environment for children with ADD, it isn't surprising that the negative behaviors which often provide the earliest indications of ADD emerge most clearly in primary classrooms. These early education years have a tremendous impact on a student's academic potential, and ADD students may require special attention to develop the basic skills which will form the foundation for future progress.

How Does ADD Affect Reading Ability?

Since learning to read requires both focused attention and strong memory, reading problems are common in ADD children. In order to read, a child must learn individual letter names and sounds as well as letter combinations. In addition, a child must become familiar with language patterns, exceptions to these patterns, and nonphonetic words (sight words). Parents and teachers may help ADD children acquire these complex skills by employing some of these suggestions.

1. Make sure the child is taught to read in a systematic fashion. Reading instruction for ADD children should be based on a structured, sequential format of lessons in combination with "high interest" materials.

A balanced reading program consists of two main components, word recognition and comprehension, and within each component there are a

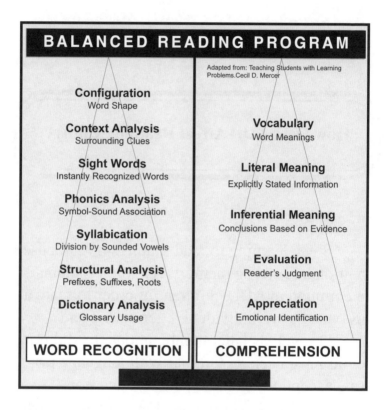

BALANCED READING PROGRAM

Adapted from: Teaching Students with Learning Problems.Cecil D. Mercer

Configuration
Word Shape

Context Analysis
Surrounding Clues

Sight Words
Instantly Recognized Words

Phonics Analysis
Symbol-Sound Association

Syllabication
Division by Sounded Vowels

Structural Analysis
Prefixes, Suffixes, Roots

Dictionary Analysis
Glossary Usage

Vocabulary
Word Meanings

Literal Meaning
Explicitly Stated Information

Inferential Meaning
Conclusions Based on Evidence

Evaluation
Reader's Judgment

Appreciation
Emotional Identification

| WORD RECOGNITION | COMPREHENSION |

number of related skills. (See Box) For example, phonics is a word recognition ability while vocabulary ranks as a comprehension skill. Both skills play equal roles in the process of reading; indeed, the two abilities must interact for reading to occur. Knowing how to "sound out" the word through phonics is pointless if the student does not know what the word means, and comprehending a definition has little use if the child cannot recognize or pronounce the word. By putting equal emphasis on mastering all the skills needed for reading, a balanced program offers teachers a flexible format to address the needs of each individual.

Repetition (seeing the same word multiple times) is a crucial component in early reading instruction, especially for the ADD child who might not be paying attention during initial instruction. Clients at Brainworks practice repetition reading in two ways. First, the students are timed as they read alphabetical lists of grade level appropriate words aloud; in order to master each list, they must pronounce each word correctly and "beat the clock" by finishing the list within a targeted time limit of two seconds per word. At the top of each list, the time goal for that column is written, and at the bottom of the list, the students record their times for each attempt.

Beat the clock!

The second type of repetition practice involves timing the students as they read short "high interest" stories (also based on appropriate levels of material) aloud. Again, students will repeat the reading during subsequent practice sessions until they reach the target time without an error. Each practice session for these exercises should last no more than five minutes at a stretch to reduce the "boredom factor" inherent to multiple readings of the same words, but students should be able to handle several short practices over the course of a day.

The key element in both of these activities is the power of the stopwatch. Not only do the target times give the children goals, but the goals also help them track their progress as times improve on each effort. Further, "beating the clock" makes the task seem more like a game to the students, and this competitive aspect encourages their persistence on a task they might otherwise view as pointless.

2. Individualized instruction during the early phases of learning to read makes a big difference in whether children master reading skills. When there is only one student, an instructor or tutor is able to review information as many times as necessary for the child to grasp the concept.

Parents should listen to the beginning reader practice reading out loud nightly.

Parents and family members can provide such individual attention through "reading out loud" practice sessions at home; the child's classroom teacher should be consulted for specific suggestions concerning the areas most in need of remediation and strategies for improvement. However, if an ADD student consistently experiences serious problems with reading and begins to lag behind his peers, parents should consider having the child evaluated for possible participation in some form of special service or resource program. Such programs offer the child a greater degree of individual attention and thus speed up the acquisition of reading skills.

3. If the child has been identified as "at risk" for reading, the child should begin intensive reading instruction as soon as possible. According to the National Center for Learning Disabilities, **"...the majority of L.D. readers are not identified until the third grade**. **This is apparently too late. Seventy-five percent of children identified after nine years of age continue to demonstrate reading difficulties throughout high school."**

This striking statistic illustrates the urgent need for "rapid response" to reading problems as soon as they become evident. Parents who are told, "Don't worry because the child will outgrow this reading

Third Grade Could Be Too Late.

problem," should seek a second opinion from a trained reading specialist before the child falls behind his peers in this most essential learning skill. While it is possible the child might "catch up" on his own, it is more likely that he will not. Waiting until third or fourth grade to address weaknesses in reading may mean the student falls so far behind that his self-esteem hits rock bottom. For the child, reading will become a source of anxiety, something to be avoided. Given the tremendous impact of reading ability on a child's future, most parents would agree that "wait and see" could be a costly mistake.

4. Brain research has shown how each individual's brain operates differently and how "inefficiencies" in certain areas of the brain can affect a child's capacity to learn. However, it is erroneous to assume a child's reading problems are automatically related to these brain inefficiencies and are therefore beyond the reach of remediation. Too often children are given broad diagnostic "catch all" labels (such as dyslexia) without first exploring other physical factors which could affect reading.

Since vision is such an integral component of reading, **a thorough visual exam by a**

visual specialist should be performed before the child begins school. In addition, hearing problems affect more than a child's ability to learn individual sounds; auditory problems also delay the development of receptive and expressive language skills. Students with auditory problems spend most of their energy trying to capture the basic meanings of words and sentences; subtle language factors such as metaphors and idioms may be lost on these individuals. **A hearing examination**, therefore, is a key factor in evaluating any child's readiness for reading instruction, but it **is especially crucial for ADDers, many of whom suffer recurring ear infections throughout their lifetimes.**

5. Building a child's sight word vocabulary is sometimes a neglected area in reading instruction. Recognizing sight words is essential for increasing reading speed in context; the fewer words a child has to stop and decode, the more fluently he will read.

Because ADD children react negatively to "boring" repetitive work, flash cards are not always the most effective method for them to learn sight words. As an alternative, children should read a list of words aloud repeatedly until they can recognize each word within three seconds. This process should be timed, and when

```
┌─────────────────────────────────────────────────┐
│            Sight Word List (25 Words)           │
│                                                 │
│   about     out      fall     hold     kind     │
│                                                 │
│   better    done     far      hot      laugh    │
│                                                 │
│   bring     draw     full     hurt     light    │
│                                                 │
│   carry     drunk    got      if       long     │
│                                                 │
│   clean     eight    grow     keep     much     │
│                                                 │
│ Goal:  50 seconds (2 seconds per word)          │
│ Your times:  _____   _____   _____ │
│                                                 │
└─────────────────────────────────────────────────┘
```

children see their times for each list decreasing, they will be more motivated to continue. A parent can get this list from the classroom teacher or buy it at a teacher's supply store.

6. Remediate the reading weaknesses of ADD children by employing strategies based on their optimum learning style. For example, children of normal intelligence who are unable to recall the names of specific alphabet letters might be helped by learning to recite the familiar "ABC song." In this way, children can use a "right brain" strength (rhythm) to reinforce a "mid-brain" deficit (symbolic interpretation).

Other children whose strengths may include kinesthetic awareness (learning through movement) can practice the alphabet with a partner by forming letter shapes with body postures. Some would enjoy creating a "dance" with motions representing different letters. (See Appendix for kinesthetic versions of the alphabet.) Tactile learners can trace letters on various surfaces, such as sand, concrete, shaving cream, or carpet, thus using their awareness of textures to reinforce their alphabet skills.

Form letters with a partner.

Another tactile exercise frequently employed at Brainworks involves having clients reach into a covered box and use their fingertips to "read" letters which have been carved on pieces of wood or cardboard. As they follow the grooves, the students must rely on their tactile sensitivity to create a visual image which they can recognize.

The index finger of the non-dominant hand feels the letter while the dominant hand writes the letter.

A young client at Brainworks who possessed a highly developed sense of touch once practiced her alphabet by arranging a length of rope on the floor in the shape of a letter. She then removed her shoes and walked barefoot on the path of the rope! The sensation helped her perceive clearly each letter's distinctive shape, and she incorporated it into her memory.

How Does ADD Affect Math Ability?

As with reading, math requires focused attention and memorization; however, we read left to right and work math problems right to left. This change can be confusing for ADDers with directionality problems. ADD children also detest  the repetition and rote drills required to master math facts; therefore, these students may also lag behind their peers in acquiring math skills. At Brainworks, we remediate math weaknesses by making the work more appealing to our clients.

Math games are more fun than drill.

Playing math "games" creates a greater interest in the subject and, consequently, a higher level of concentration on the part of the student. In addition, past failures and frustrations with math assignments and tests can provoke "math anxiety" reactions from students, some of whom literally break into a sweat at the sight of computation problems. The level of stress experienced by these youngsters interferes with their ability to learn, but reviewing math skills through game formats teaches them to approach numbers in a more relaxed and comfortable manner.

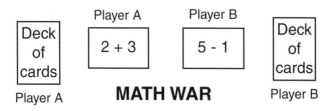

1. One popular math game at Brainworks is **Math War**. This game is played with a special deck of cards; instead of numbers and suits, these cards are labeled with basic math fact problems, such as 2+3 and 5-1. Basically, the game is played the same way as regular "War" or "Battle" card games, except the student must know the answers to the math fact problems in order to know who wins each hand.

The deck of cards is divided equally among the players, and the cards are kept face down until the play begins. Simultaneously, all the players turn their top card over to reveal the math fact computations; the students "work" the problems on these cards aloud, and the card which has the highest number for the answer wins. The winner scoops up the cards and places them in a "capture" pile.

If two players have cards with identical answers (such as 3+3 and 7-1), they lay three cards face down and turn over the fourth card; the person with the highest number on the fourth card "captures" all the opponent's cards. At the end of the game, the students count the number of cards in each player's capture pile to determine the winner of the contest.

```
┌─────────────────────────────────────────────┐
│              MEMORY MATCH                     │
│                                               │
│  ┌────┐   ┌────┐   ┌──────┐  ┌────┐           │
│  │    │   │    │   │ 6X3  │  │    │           │
│  └────┘   └────┘   └──────┘  └────┘           │
│                                               │
│  ┌────┐   ┌────┐   ┌──────┐  ┌────┐           │
│  │ 18 │   │    │   │ 4X6  │  │    │           │
│  └────┘   └────┘   └──────┘  └────┘           │
│                                               │
│  ┌────┐   ┌────┐   ┌──────┐  ┌────┐           │
│  │    │   │    │   │  24  │  │    │           │
│  └────┘   └────┘   └──────┘  └────┘           │
│                                               │
└─────────────────────────────────────────────┘
```

2. Playing **"memory match"** with problem and answer cards is another alternative for practicing math facts. For this game, answer cards are added to the deck so students can match the answers to the problems.

The game begins by shuffling and placing the cards face down on the table. The children turn over two cards per turn, reciting the math problem(s) aloud while doing so. If the problem card's solution matches an answer card, the student keeps the matched cards, and whoever has the most pairs at the end is the winner.

During the early part of the game, finding a match will be a coincidence, but as the game continues, the student's ability to recall where he saw the matching card adds a visual memory component to the competition. In fact, since visual memory is often a strength for ADD students, they may have an advantage over their non-ADD opponents in terms of that phase of the game!

3. Manipulatives, such as dice, cards, counting beans, pegboards, etc., are excellent for teaching math facts to ADD children. The hands-on component of such tools helps them focus, and the use of concrete materials may help students make the transition to abstract math concepts more easily. Several excellent activity books currently on the market offer creative methods for using manipulatives in basic math activities. Some of the books we frequently use at Brainworks include **About Teaching Mathematics** by Marilyn Burns (Math Solutions Publications, 1992), **Mathematics Their Way** by Mary Baratta-Lorton (Addison-Wesley Publishing, 1996) and **Developing Number Concepts Using Unifix Cubes** by Kathy Richardson (Addison-Wesley Publishing, 1971).

4. Some ADD children miss the answers to math problems because they don't pay attention to the signs of the problems, particularly on homework or tests which mix addition, subtraction, multiplication, and division problems. For example, a homework assignment may have four addition problems in a row, but when the next problem is "5-3," the ADD student may answer "8" because he didn't notice the sign indicated subtraction.

Before beginning to work on an assignment, the ADD child should highlight the math signs for each problem according to a color code, such as pink for subtraction and blue for addition. The highlights will help the student focus on the sign for each problem. (Parents may want to negotiate with their child's teacher to have the same color-coding system used with in-class tests.)

5. Another problem for ADD children who have handwriting problems has to do with keeping their columns of numbers correctly aligned when working on computations involving two and three digit numbers.

Notice how columns are not aligned.
$\overset{3}{3}92$
x54
1 5 6 8
19600
125,208

Our clients often find it helpful to turn their note-book paper **sideways** so they can use the lines on the paper as "guides" to keep their columns in order. Another option is to have the child use graph paper to line up the numbers; if possible, the graph paper should have different colors for the vertical and horizontal lines. Again, parents need to consult with the classroom teacher about using this tip on tests and on homework assignments.

Often ADDers need help keeping their numbers in the proper column.

$$\overset{3}{3}92$$
$$\underline{\times 54}$$
$$1568$$
$$\underline{19600}$$
$$125,208$$

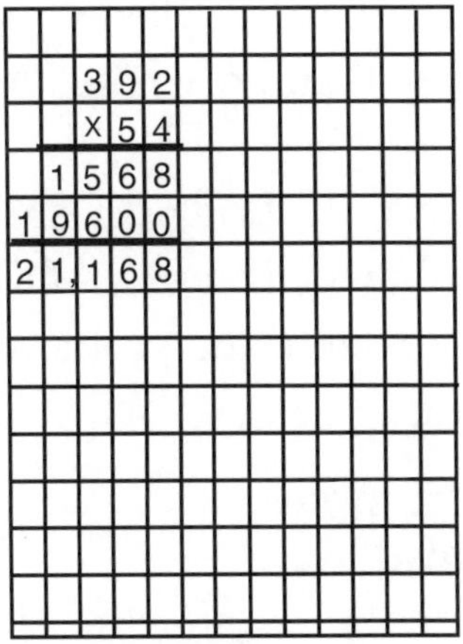

Use graph paper.

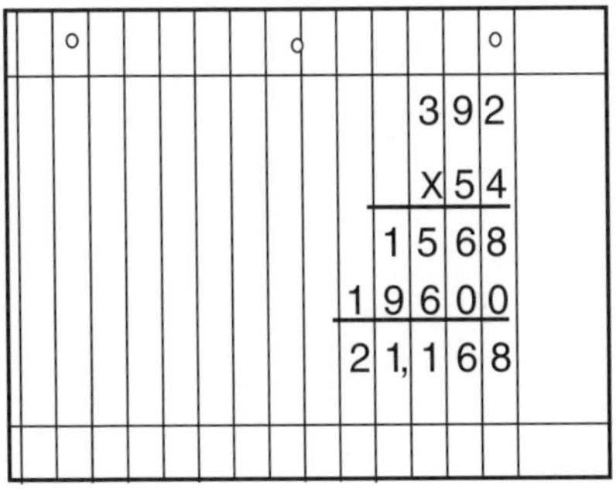

ADDers can turn paper to help keep columns straight.

6. Research shows that over 70% of all multiplication errors occur when students must multiply and add the number carried before they write an answer.

$$\overset{\scriptstyle 7}{4}9$$
$$\underline{\times 8}$$

9 x 8 = 72. Write down the 2 and carry the 7. The step of 4 x 8 + 7 is hard for most ADDers to visualize. We suggest that third and fourth grade students practice doing problems like 3 x 7 + 5, 4 x 8 + 7,   6 x 9 + 8 in their heads. Mastery would be achieved when they could give the answer within 6 seconds.

7. Long division requires several sequenced steps. ADDers forget to repeat the steps until the problem is finished or forget the steps.

Example mistake:

$$7\,\overline{)161} \quad \begin{array}{r} 20 \;\; r\,21 \\ \hline \end{array}$$
$$\underline{14}$$
$$21$$

We recommend to teach a mnemonic for <u>d</u>ivide, <u>m</u>ultiply, <u>s</u>ubtract, and <u>b</u>ring down. <u>D</u>ear <u>M</u>iss <u>S</u>ally <u>B</u>rown or <u>D</u>ad, <u>M</u>other, <u>S</u>ister, <u>B</u>rother.

8. Many ADDers have problems recognizing when to borrow when subtracting.

$$\begin{array}{r} 2\,4\,2\,7 \\ -\,1\,6\,8\,6 \\ \hline 1\,2\,6\,1 \end{array}$$
Many ADDers will subtract all the smaller numbers from the larger number.

$$\begin{array}{r} 2\,4\,2\,7 \\ -\,1\,6\,8\,6 \end{array}$$
We recommend that they highlight only the numbers that must be changed before they do the computation.

9. Adding three or more numbers involves adding an "unseen" two-digit number to a "seen" one-digit number. This is difficult for many ADDers.

$$\begin{array}{r} 4783 \\ 2989 \\ +\ 276 \end{array}$$
12 - "unseen" + 6 = 18

Solution:
We recommend that ADDers practice this skill before working these types of problems. The student writes down a series of one digit numbers like: 9, 6, 4, 7, 8, 5

The teacher calls out a two digit number like "16." The students would then add in their heads 16 to each of the numbers and write down the answer. ADDers need to practice mental exercises; often this skill is a weak area for them. It may take daily practice for the student to listen to a number, add it to a number on a page, and solve it mentally within 3-5 seconds. Five minutes daily practice could produce miraculous results.

10. When adding two or more numbers that involves carrying, ADDers may have problems with the carrying process. They may reverse the numbers when carrying.

	A.	In problem A, the student adds 7+6+8 = 21. The 2 is carried.		B.	In problem B, the student carried the 1, not the 2.

A.
```
   2
   37
   16
 + 48
  101
```
In problem A, the student adds 7+6+8 = 21. The 2 is carried.

B.
```
   1
   37
   16
 + 48
   92
```
In problem B, the student carried the 1, not the 2.

Solution options:
For some ADDers, they may prefer to carry at the bottom rather than at the top.

```
   37
   16
 + 48
    2
  101
```

Another suggestion is that they add left to right adding the tens first then the ones. This tactic eliminates the need to carry.

```
   37
   16
 + 48
   80  (tens)
   21  (ones)
  101
```

11. Long division requires neat columns and knowing where to put your answers.

A.
```
      23 r0
  7/161
      14
      21
      21
       0
```
In A, the 2 goes over the 6 because 7 went into 16.

B.
```
     203 r0
  7/161
      14
      21
      21
       0
```
In B, the person makes a major mistake because the 2 is over the 1.

3 7 2, 1 0 6, 8 5 4

green for millions

red for thousands

blue for hundreds

12. Have students write numbers in a variety of colors and read the numbers out loud until they can read and write without any hesitation. ADD children are often right hemisphere dominant. Color sensitivity is a strength of the right hemisphere, so using colors can help them remember the place value of numbers.

13. Because math requires so much intense concentration for some of our ADDers, we may negotiate with teachers to assign fewer problems. Instead of 30 problems for homework, we will suggest that ADDers do the odd problems only. These problems, however, count twice as much if they make a mistake.

Introduction

Strategies for Poor Writing Skills

Writing is a complex process requiring the interaction of a number of different abilities, many of which constitute areas of difficulty for the ADD child. Sitting in a chair to write requires adequate upper body strength; writing on lined paper requires both visual perception and efficient motor skills. Simultaneously, the writer must utilize long-term memory in order to recall how each letter looks as well as the correct sequence of the letters within the word.

Sustained attention is an additional requirement for writing with which the ADD child struggles. Halfway through a sentence, the child's focus on what is being written may be lost in the rapid fire of thoughts and ideas which keep flashing through his mind. Having forgotten what he is going to say, the student starts over, only to

ADDer battles: outside rapid firing thoughts and his writing assignment.

have the interference repeat itself; the inevitable result is frustration.

Organizational skills, always a challenge for ADDers, are important for establishing the proper sequence of words within the sentence (syntax) as well as the best arrangement of sentences within a paragraph. ADDers also have problems focusing on details, a characteristic which hinders the development of proofreading skills and leads to problems with spelling, punctuation, and grammar.

All these elements and phases of the writing process have to be systematically introduced to the ADD child and practiced frequently for mastery. Parents and teachers should be aware of what Dr. Sam Goldstein has called the ADD child's **"inability to benefit from experience."** Concepts and guidelines which other children might pick up during three writing practices may take an ADD child nine (or more) writing practices to absorb. As for the permanent acquisition of skills, ADD children often seem like **"Teflon Students"** because knowledge just

Teflon Students

doesn't seem to "stick" with them as it does their peers. For these students, mastery of a writing skill (such as writing topic sentences for paragraphs) should be considered a temporary acquisition which will require regular review and extended practices.

Ironically, some ADDers develop into exceptional writers. These individuals learn to apply their creative talents and heightened sensory awareness to written formats, and, given encouragement and direction, they produce prose and poetry of tremendous depth and sensitivity. Unfortunately, many other ADD students become so discouraged by their struggles with written expression that they never reach this level of achievement. The following questions have been divided into three sections, each dealing with a different component of writing skills. By applying some of these suggestions, teachers and parents may help an ADD child experience "more success with less stress" when writing.

What Physical Factors Affect The Handwriting Of An ADD Child?

1. Writing is a physical as well as a mental activity, an often overlooked fact which has special significance for **ADDers who may have to exert tremendous amounts of physical energy in order to sit at a desk and hold still.** This concept is quite alien to the experience of non-ADDers, and, indeed, it does seem to fly in the face of logic–if motion requires effort, then shouldn't being motionless also be effortless? However, since the "natural state" for ADD children *is* motion, the act of holding still in a seat long enough to write a paragraph can be incredibly draining for these students. They often end up slumped in their seats with their heads resting sideways on the desktops—an incredibly awkward posture which can interfere with their ability to read as well as write. This posture puts

Sitting at a desk can drain the ADDer of energy.

serious strain on the visual system and the muscles in the neck and back. Usually this posture also causes students to develop an awkward pencil grasp.

Therefore, it is crucial that the ADD child develop the upper-body strength and stamina necessary for writing or any prolonged "seat work" task. At Brainworks, we evaluate our younger clients for their level of physical strength before they begin writing practices. The exercises suggested below provide a way to check a child's physical readiness for writing; they were taken from **Sensory Integration and the Child** by Dr. Jean Ayres.

A. Have the child lie on his back on an exercise mat. He should raise his head and upper body slightly, extend his arms straight ahead, and hold both legs off the mat. Note that the hands do not touch the legs. To "master" this exercise, the student should be able to hold this position for 30 seconds. If the student cannot hold the position, he should work on strengthening exercises to develop these muscles until he does achieve mastery.

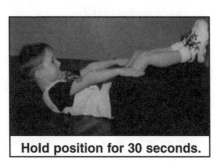
Hold position for 30 seconds.

B. Have the child lie on his stomach. He should raise his upper body and legs, extend his arms out from the body like wings on an airplane, and keep his stomach on the mat. He should be able to hold this position for 30 seconds; if he cannot, he should work on strengthening exercises to develop these muscles until he has mastered this skill.

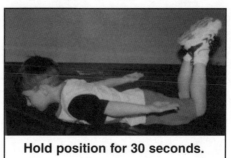

Hold position for 30 seconds.

2. Because nearly all ADDers have trouble with handwriting, it's important to focus on establishing a proper pencil grasp as soon as the child learns to write. Correcting a poor grip is possible when the student is seven years old, but trying to correct the problem when the student is seventeen years old is almost impossible.

An awkward, painful pencil grip has a devastating effect on a student's ability to succeed academically, particularly in middle school and secondary school where classes require increasingly greater volumes of written work. If writing is slow or painful, the student will limit how much he writes on tests, will avoid written home-work assignments, and will be unable to take adequate notes from lectures.

A painful pencil grasp affects academic production.

Although teachers in primary grade classes usually evaluate student handwriting by checking the pages of practice exercises, such evaluations often won't detect problems students may have with the physical process of writing. However, it is possible for teachers to ascertain if students are experiencing pain while writing by having the class execute a timed copying exercise.

The quick brown fox
jumped over the lazy dog.
The quick brown fox......

Two Minute Test

The quick brown fox
jumped over the lazy
dog. The quick...

A. Give the class a sentence to copy repeatedly within a **two minute** time span. They should write as quickly as they can, but they should also make sure the words are readable.

B. Begin the timing. At the end of the two minutes, tell the class to stop writing and have each student count how many words were copied. Then repeat the exercise for another two minute timing.

C. Throughout the copying and immediately afterwards, note any students who shake their hands, rub their wrists, pull on their fingers, or crack their knuckles. Ask these students where it hurts. If they experience pain after writing for less than five minutes, these children need to work on adjusting how they hold their pencils and/or how they position their paper or bodies while writing.

3. Another way for teachers to detect potential "pain problems" with student handwriting in the above exercise is to have the students write the copied words with several sheets of "pad paper" behind the worksheet page. After the exercise, the teacher should turn the student pages over and run a finger over the paper. If the words can be felt as severe "ridges" which almost penetrate the paper, these indentations indicate the student has applied an excessive amount of pressure indicating physical stress.

Further observation will probably reveal the child has developed a "death grip" pencil grasp. By clutching the writing instrument so intensely, the student creates "white knuckles" very quickly

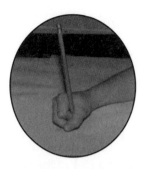

Holding pencil at the point with a death grip.

and the end result is pain in the fingers and the wrist. As our clients work on reducing the tension in their pencil grip, they often spend a few minutes exercising their hands with therapy putty before starting a handwriting practice. This "warm-up" helps loosen the muscles in their hands and relaxes their grasp. (Parents can ask their pediatrician to order therapy putty from a medical supply catalog; it is also available in some drug stores.)

4. Trying to alter a child's pencil grip is a task which must be approached very delicately in order to be successful. Handwriting is a very personal issue for almost any human being. It represents each person's distinctive individuality; it is "who we are" on paper. (Consider the significance our society places on a person's signature when it appears on letters, contracts, and checks!)

When children enter school, they do begin a process of structured education. They also begin a process of personal development as they

"My Handwriting Style Makes Me Unique."

establish identities apart from the family unit. Handwriting style is an expression of each youngster's desire for "uniqueness," and because of this sensitive dynamic, students may react very negatively to attempts to change the way they write. Yet, unless the child cooperates in the effort, no improvement will occur.

When presenting the issue of handwriting remediation to a child, teachers and parents should stress the concept of **changing the pencil grip to reduce pain and fatigue**. A practice session will fail if the supervising adult says,"Look how terrible your writing looks! You're holding the pencil the wrong way. Let me show you the right way to hold it." This sort of comment sounds like nagging to the student, who will quickly "turn

off" the lesson and reject the advice. Better results will come if the adult watches the child write for a few minutes and then asks quietly, "Where does your hand hurt?" This approach is less critical and less threatening to the child's ego; moreover, it demonstrates a level of concern and empathy for his plight.

Be careful how you approach handwriting remediation.

As the child describes "where it hurts most," the adult should listen carefully and then suggest ways to realign the grasp on the pencil to reduce the discomfort. It's also important to explain to the child that the new grip will probably feel awkward at first because it's not the way he is accustomed to holding the pencil, but in time he will adjust.

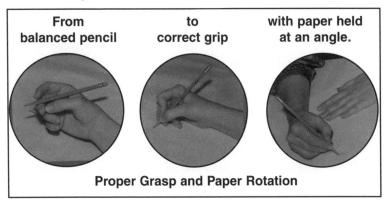

| From balanced pencil | to correct grip | with paper held at an angle. |

Proper Grasp and Paper Rotation

    5. A common pencil grip problem for children occurs when they try to hold the pencil too near the point. (see pages 249 and 251.) At Brainworks, we refer to the lead pencil point as the "alligator" and the exposed wood area at the sharpened end as the "alligator zone." Our clients

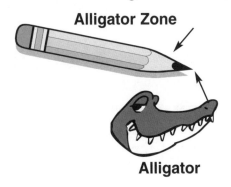

Alligator Zone

Alligator

are admonished to "stay out of the alligator zone" as they practice handwriting! If a student tends to get too close to the pencil end while writing, we quietly tap the pencil and say, "alligator," to remind the student that he has slipped into the alligator zone. In some cases a small rubber band on the pencil shaft to mark the "stopping place" can serve as a reminder.

6. An important element in establishing a good pencil grasp is learning how to place the paper being written on at an angle. The paper should be rotated slightly instead of sitting squarely in front of the student; without this rotation, the writer cannot see what she is writing, so she will either "hook" her wrist and/or strain her neck as she writes. Both of these writing positions can cause pain in the body leading to exhaustion.

   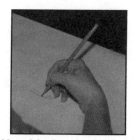

Head too close to the paper   **Hand in hooked position**

To see the proper paper placement (See picture on page 255.), the student should put a dot in the center of the top line of the paper and then draw a one inch line on each side of the dot. While holding the pencil tip on the dot, the student rotates the top of the paper to the left until both lines are visible. (Left-handed students will need to rotate the paper to the right.)

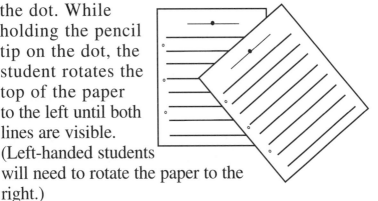

The student should note this angle and during writing practices should check to make sure the position is maintained. Because some students will move the paper out of the position unconsciously as they work, they may need to tape the corners into position until they grow accustomed to writing at this angle.

7. ADD children often become so focused on shaping their letters and keeping track of the words that they ignore the left and right hand margins of the paper. Often, they continue writing past the right hand margin, and some of them even continue writing past the edge of the paper! Help students become more conscious of margins by drawing green ("go") lines on the left side and red ("stop") lines on the right side margins.

8. Teach the ADD child to use computer word-processing programs as soon as possible. Parents should purchase keyboarding instruction

programs that offer games as reinforcement and encourage the child to practice 10-15 minutes daily as a homework assignment. When the student can type approximately 30 words per minute, he will be given an outlet for expression that can lead to academic and personal success. Too many students are trapped inside their handwriting disability.

What Role Does Memory Play In Handwriting Skills Of The ADD Child?

1. Letter recall can be a problem for ADD children. Having spent two years memorizing the 26 upper-case and 26 lower-case manuscript (printed) letters, they are then "cursed by cursive," for they now have 52 more letter shapes to learn! Children without ADD (or other learning problems) seem to learn these letters almost by osmosis; after seeing the letters a few times, non-ADD children are able to recall them readily.

However, ADD children may need repeated practice in letter recall and should spend at least five minutes daily writing the letters from memory. The following is a good practice routine:

A. First, have them print all the upper-case manuscript letters. The goal is to do this in 78 seconds or less (3 seconds per letter); time them as they work toward this goal. Record any letters they recall incorrectly.

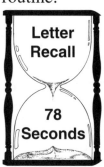

Letter Recall

78 Seconds

B. Follow the same procedure with lower-case manuscript, upper case, cursive and lower-case cursive letters.

Of course, the real challenge in having ADD children practice letter recall is keeping their attention focused during what is admittedly a rather boring activity. Having the 78 second goal helps since it makes the exercise competitive, but the student may need some other incentives. For example, provide the student with pens and pencils which write in a variety of colors and try colored paper as well, or play music during the practice session. Parents and teachers could also "break the monotony" of letter recall practice by switching to different writing materials entirely, such as chalk and sidewalks instead of pencil and paper.

Play music with a variety of beats to practice letter recall.

2. Another aspect of memory which affects the handwriting of ADD children is **directionality**. This skill requires the child to recall where the "starting point" for drawing each letter is and in what directions the pencil will move to shape the letter. Many ADD children will automatically start writing at the bottom of the line to draw a letter

such as "f," thus making the process of writing awkward. The ADDer reduces directional choices by starting on the only constant space on the paper – the line. Remembering to start letters at the proper spot and to follow through by moving the pencil in the most efficient manner is an ability which must be cultivated in the ADD child.

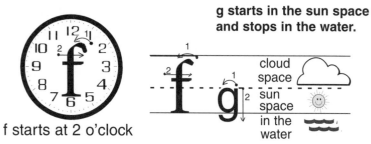

f starts at 2 o'clock

g starts in the sun space and stops in the water.

cloud space
sun space
in the water

f starts in the clouds and stops on the bottom of the sun space.

To assist our young clients in their ability to recall the directionality involved in shaping letters, we employ some basic guidelines in their handwriting practices. First, we mark a green dot to signal the "starting point" for the letter, and the client places the pencil at this spot to begin drawing the letter. Next, we use arrows to show the client the direction which the pencil line will follow. Finally, we often have the client verbalize the motions being followed aloud as each letter is drawn. A child drawing the letter "f" would say, "Start at 2 on the clock and go around until 12. Then draw the line down to 6. Then lift the pencil and draw from 9 to 3." Another student may find it easier to draw the "f" by starting in the cloud space and stopping on the line before the water. The next line is drawn on the line between the cloud and sun spaces.

3. During writing assignments, some children may need a copy of the letters taped to their desks until they master letter recall. However, don't allow them to use this "desk copy" during letter recall tests.

What Can Improve The Composition Skills Of ADD Students?

1. ADD children often have problems with composition because they try to do "everything at once." They want to create ideas and write them into a perfect paragraph in one pass, but this haste (as usual) works against them. If they begin working without planning, they will hit a brick wall when they don't know "what I'm saying next" will be. If they try to compose sentences and simultaneously check their spelling, they will both lose their train of thought and misspell words. Therefore, these children need to be taught how to approach writing as a series of different tasks which lead to the final product. To accomplish this, instruction should break the writing process into three distinct phases.

Writing Steps

C Proofread the Paragraph.

B Compose the Rough Draft.

A Brainstorm the Topic.

A. Brainstorm the topic.

In this phase, the student comes up with as many ideas as possible which relate to the subject. At Brainworks, our students often use "webbing" (sometimes called "mind-mapping") to document their ideas as they develop. The web below illustrates ideas created for a character description.

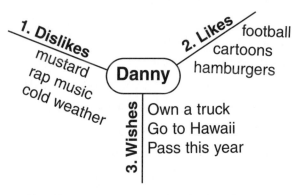

B. Compose the rough draft.

After completing the brainstorming phase, the students should choose which ideas will be used and which will be discarded. The next decision is in what order will the ideas be used; this arrangement can be noted on the web by marking "1, 2, 3," etc. next to the branches on the web sheet.

They then make the "sloppy copy" by converting the web ideas into sentences of the paragraph. They should be concerned with transferring the ideas and making sure they write complete sentences. They should NOT be concerned with spelling or punctuation during this phase, however.

C. Proofread the paragraph.

Students should check the paragraph for usage errors. In primary grades, the type of errors they will be capable of spotting and correcting should be limited to only the most basic errors. At Brainworks, we train our students in the "COPS" strategy presented in **Teaching Students with Learning Problems** by Cecil D. and Ann Mercer. (Merrill/Macmillan Publishing, 1993).

C-Capitalization
O-Overall appearance
P-Punctuation
S-Spelling

(See the Appendix for additional information on this strategy.)

Finally, when the child rewrites the rough draft, the teacher should encourage neatness; however, it's a good idea to allow the student to use caret insertion marks (∧) to insert omissions. Otherwise, the child may end up rewriting the entire paragraph multiple times, a frustrating process which will result in a fear and loathing of writing assignments. (In fact, children with perfectionist tendencies sometimes despise writing, because they rewrite an entire paragraph several times because a single word is missing!)

2. Since all children have unique experiential backgrounds, **assigning topics for writing exercises can be tricky**. It's not safe to assume that a child understands a topic simply because other children of the same age know about it. For example, a child who is asked to write a paragraph about oceans will be handicapped if he has never been to the beach or has never read about ocean life. Also, reading is how people acquire vocabulary, and if the ADD child has had reading problems, he will usually have writing problems as well.

Children should have several options for writing topics whenever they work on compositions. Before beginning a writing exercise, instructors should discuss the topics with the class to be sure the children understand the options.

3. Have ADD children use a tape recorder during the prewriting or "brainstorming" part of the writing process. This strategy can be beneficial in many ways. ADD children often report their writing 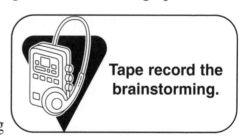 **Tape record the brainstorming.** fingers can't move as fast as their minds, but a tape recorder will capture the ideas which otherwise would be lost. Another benefit to taping is they

can refer to the tape if they are distracted or interrupted in the middle of a sentence.

4. When ADD students work on writing assignments, they tend to "think out loud" as they commit words to paper, a process which helps them organize their thoughts and maintain their concentration, but they may also disturb the concentration of other people in the vicinity.

Since thinking aloud is essentially a positive behavior, teachers and parents should not discourage the practice; however, they may want to encourage the student to "lower the volume" on the self-talk. The first step is to have the adult and the student develop **a non-verbal signal** (such as a gesture or placing a colored card on the desk) to cue "switch to whisper." During work periods, the adult monitors the volume of the one-person conversation, signaling the student whenever his voice

ADDers will need a signal to lower volume on self-talk.

goes above a whisper–which will be often at the start of the training. Eventually, the student's awareness of the sound level will increase, and "muttering" will replace shouting.

A more immediate remedy for the classroom teacher would be to create a separate **concentration zone** for the ADD student to work on writing assignments. This area should be set up to soundproof the ADDer from other students and can be called the ADDers private office.

5. If the ADD child has difficulty with sentence structure, a good practice exercise is to give him sentences with "scrambled" words and have him put them in the proper order to make sense. Or, have the student work on "sentence combining" exercises where he combines two or more basic sentences into more complex structures. For example:

> The dog is brown.
> The dog is sleeping.
> The sleeping is quiet.
> "The brown dog sleeps quietly."

6. Assign "How to..." paragraphs to illus-

Recipes require sequential steps.

trate the importance of sentence order within a paragraph. Steps in even simple "non-cooking" recipes (such as sandwiches or breakfast dishes) must be followed in a specific order to prevent disaster! To prove this point, the teacher could mix up the steps in a recipe and model the outcome for the class.

In another sequence exercise, the students could be given a set of "scrambled" instructions for a familiar process or game. Their tasks will be to rearrange the steps in the proper order.

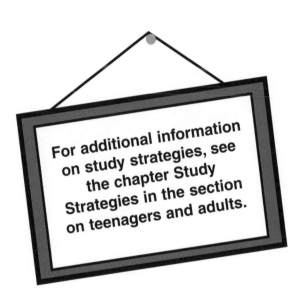

For additional information on study strategies, see the chapter Study Strategies in the section on teenagers and adults.

PERSONAL POINTERS

INTRODUCTION

 What Are Positive Motivators For An ADD Child?

 What Behaviors Can An ADD Child Control?

 Why Would An Active ADD Child Hate Gym Class?

 Does Traveling With An ADD Child Have To Be Disasterous?

 How Can "Physical Restlessness" Be A Positive Factor In Learning?

 How Can Teachers Accommodate The Hyper Child In The Classroom?

What Are Positive Motivators For An ADD Child?

Many ADD children experience life as a series of frustrations and failed efforts, and children who fail repeatedly become afraid. Once anyone tries to do something and fails, the natural tendency is to shy away from future attempts. It  may take only a few failed endeavors to "sour" a child's attitude for the rest of his life. If someone comments about a child's "clumsiness," that child may grow into an adult who avoids gymnastic exercises or dancing lessons. Or, if an adult jokes about how badly a youngster reads aloud, the child may never learn to "read for pleasure."

Life is a series of successes and failed efforts.

It's important for **all** children to have positive self-images and to feel motivated, but the ADD child may need more direction in these areas than his non-ADD peers require. The following tips offer a variety of ways to put a "positive spin" on personal development.

1. The most effective remedy for fear is success. When the child has negative feelings about an activity, "replace" the bad feelings by associating the activity with pleasant experiences. For example, if reading assigned materials from school overwhelms and stresses a student, take the child to the library and help him choose books on topics he finds interesting. Then sit with the child

 in a comfortable environment and take turns reading from the books. If the child has a hard time pronouncing some words, don't pressure him to stop in the middle of the sentence and "sound out" the word; instead, pronounce the word for the student in a "matter of fact" voice and let him continue reading without making judgments.

Create a pleasant environment to replace bad feelings.

2. If a child has success in some parts of life, the positive energy gained from achievement will transfer to other areas which are more difficult for her. Many ADD children are creatively gifted in art, theater, and music, but other ADDers may be talented athletes, mechanics, storytellers, animal trainers, campers, etc. Encourage the ADD child to find and pursue activities for which she has an affinity and celebrate her successes.

3. Once a child has developed an interest in an activity and has experienced success in it, don't threaten to remove her from the activity or to prevent her from participating as a form of punishment. This high-interest activity should be consid-

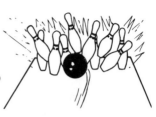

High-interest activities are a necessity to the ADDer's emotional well-being.

ered as much a necessity to the child's emotional well-being as food is considered a necessity to her physical well-being.

4. Carefully evaluate the ADD child's social development and emotional maturity before enrolling him in team sports such as football, basketball, soccer, and baseball. An ADDer typically behaves as a "lone wolf" rather than a "team player," and the pressure of having the team's success or failure tied to the ADDer's performance can inhibit his efforts during competition. When criticism from players, coaches, or spectators is heaped upon an already fragile sense of self-worth, the result may be devastating.

On the other hand, physical activity offers a wide range of benefits for ADD students, and parents of younger ADDers should consider introducing their children to sports which focus

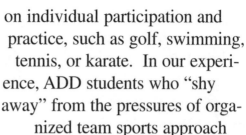

on individual participation and practice, such as golf, swimming, tennis, or karate. In our experience, ADD students who "shy away" from the pressures of organized team sports approach these activities with much more enthusiasm. When practiced on a regular basis, these exercises enhance much more than muscle development. For example, karate develops a person's balance and coordination, but it also improves listening skills, concentration, self-confidence, and spatial awareness–all in a structured format with clearly defined goals and instant feedback from instructors.

Many ADDers prefer individual sports more than group sports.

5. Find one reason every day to praise the child. Make sure the praise is specific. Instead of "You're a good kid," say "We appreciate the way you helped us fix breakfast this morning." Or, "It's fun to watch you play that new video game because you've learned it so quickly!" Also, be sure to praise effort and not just results. For example, "We're very impressed by how hard you've worked on practicing for the recital," or "We know you put a lot of time into your science project, and we love your dedication."

In addition, avoid linking praise statements to criticism with what might be called " **Yes...BUT** comments." This situation occurs when an adult attempts to "soften the blow" of criticism by leading off with a positive statement. For instance, "**Yes**, we know you're trying your best to be organized, **BUT** your room is still a trashy mess." The strategy often fails on two levels. It doesn't "soften the blow" at all; the point of the statement still focuses on the child's failure, and that's the only part of the remark the ADDer will remember. Moreover, it creates a feeling of hopelessness: "I try my best, and it's never good enough." While it is important for students to focus on areas which need improvement, it is not healthy to follow every positive comment with

a critical comment. In order for a positive statement to produce a positive result, it must be given unconditionally as "uncontaminated praise."

Finally, writing a note of praise to the child can be much more effective than saying the compliment aloud. "Putting it

Danny–

I'm so pleased with how hard you studied for your history test.

Mom

in writing" signifies a greater level of commitment, and the child can refer to written praise more than once. "Surprise" the child with notes of praise in the student's lunchbox, notebook, or backpack; put a note on his pillow, on the bathroom mirror, or on a favorite toy or game.

6. Comparing a child to other children can be very damaging to a child's self-esteem, particularly if the children involved are siblings. Every individual possesses a distinctive set of strengths and weaknesses, even within family groups, and comparing two such individuals may end up making both of them unhappy. The child who is told, "Your brother/sister never had these problems with math" will feel inadequate and resentful; on the other hand, the child used as the "measuring stick" in the comparison may chafe under the pressure to "be perfect."

Instead of resorting to comparison, stress the unique aspects of the child's personality and strengths. "No one can make me laugh the way you do!" Or, "Only you could make a sandwich this tasty!"

7. "Labeling" a child can be very detrimental to self-esteem, even if the label seems to be a positive one. As children develop their sense of personal identity, they incorporate the labels given

"You are the genius in the family."

to them by others into their behaviors. Thus, a child who is called "stupid" sees himself as someone destined to fail at school—so why fight fate by trying to learn? On the other hand, a child who is constantly described as a "genius" is placed on a pedestal which is sure to collapse. Inevitably, he will be faced with a task which is difficult for him and which requires a certain amount of "trial and error" to overcome; however, since his self-concept as a genius will permit no errors, he will not pursue the challenge to completion.

ADD Strengths	ADD Deficiencies
_____	_____
_____	_____
_____	_____
_____	_____
_____	_____
_____	_____
_____	_____

Rather than classifying the ADD child as a "type" of person, sit down with him and help him make a list of his strengths and present deficiencies; in fact, it would be a good idea for parents to "model" the exercise by making their own lists first. When the ADD child composes his own lists, the chances are he will list **more** deficiencies than strengths because he may have heard more criticisms than compliments in his brief life. Encourage him to see more of his positive qualities and work with him on strategies which employ his strengths to remediate or compensate for a deficiency. For example, if he loves music but does poorly on spelling tests, have him sing syllables as he studies, using high notes for vowels and low notes for consonants.

8. Obtain grade level appropriate biographies about successful people who have overcome challenges such as ADD, learning disabilities, or other problems. A librarian may be able to suggest titles, but books about Thomas Edison, Ben Franklin, and Winston Churchill (all likely ADDers) may give the child an ADD "hero" with whom he can identify.

Discover what ADD traits Benjamin Franklin had.

9. At least once a week, schedule special activities or outings with no "behavorial strings" attached. Don't make "good behavior" an eternal

prerequisite for a day of fun; it's a great way to show the child unconditional love and acceptance.

Weekly one-on-one time with the child could last from fifteen minutes to hours.

What Behaviors Can An
ADD Child Control?

The terms "ADD" and "behavior" seem inseparable. The diagnosis of ADD is based largely upon behavioral observations, and throughout their lifetimes, the classic behavior patterns of ADD individuals affect their ability to perform at school and at work, their relationships with others, their self-image, and their physical and mental health. In short, behavior is more than how we act–it is who we are.

A list of negative ADD behaviors is remarkably easy to compile, and most of our clients can effortlessly rattle off a list of their flaws. (After all, people have been telling them "what's wrong" with them since they were old enough to remember.) Their actions and responses have confounded and exasperated the corrective measures of their parents and teachers over and

Hey, buddy, did anybody tell you that you are a jerk?

over again. Eventually some of these students incorporate the "problem child" personality into their personal identity as a defense mechanism. This "I'm a bad seed, so why fight it?" perspective leads to still more behavior problems, followed by more recriminations. How can this vicious cycle be stopped?

1. A key issue for adults trying to improve a child's negative ADD behaviors is delineated by ADD experts Dr. Sam Goldstein and Dr. Michael Goldstein in their book, **Hyperactivity: Why Won't My Child Pay Attention?** In order to change the behaviors of an ADD child, parents and teachers need to **distinguish between behaviors resulting from incompetence and behaviors resulting from noncompliance or disobedience**. This distinction is crucial since the two situations require drastically different management approaches. As the Goldsteins point out, "Problems of incompetence must be treated with education and skill building. Problems of noncompliance are best firmly, consistently, and appropriately punished."

Is the ADDer incompetent or noncompliant?

Most behavior problems of ADD children do seem to stem from incompetancies, but the fact that these youngsters have ADD does not exclude them from the normal childhood pattern of "testing the limits" by indulging in deliberate acts of disobedience. In order for parents or teachers to evaluate whether a behavior stems from lack of skills or from defiance, they must educate themselves regarding the skill weaknesses associated with ADD. The next step involves applying this knowledge to the real-life behavior issues facing the child. Consider the following behaviors and ask, "Does this situation require punishment or problem-solving?"

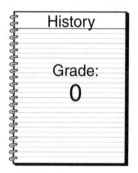

A. The child receives several zeros on history assignments because the papers and/or textbook "disappeared in transit" somewhere between home and school.

B. The child receives several zeros on history assignments because she wrote down the wrong page numbers and due dates.

C. The child receives several zeros on history assignments because she spent her scheduled "homework  time" each evening drawing colorful pictures which portray dinosaurs devouring her history teacher.

In the first two instances, the problem is clearly based on incompetence; organizing and tracking such details are classic ADD problem areas. The third situation, however, may not seem so clear-cut, and it deserves a closer look. Some parents might say, "Well, I know ADD children have problems staying on task, and they tend to be creative and visual. Therefore, it's not fair to hold her responsible for doing homework which bores her."

At Brainworks, we consider this sort of rationale to be "dangerous thinking," for it assumes the child is congenitally unable to meet expectations or work within guidelines. Moreover, it provides the student with built-in validation for choosing the path of least resistance, a childhood habit which often translates into a "lifestyle of failure" for an ADD adult. *If* the assignment is within the student's intellectual capabilities, *if* the task can be accomplished within a reasonable time frame, and *if* there is a structured time and place established for the "homework routine," then the ADD student should be held accountable for his actions.

Some ADD children become adept at rationalizing their transgressions. One of our clients regularly ignored his homework obligations so he could watch television every night. He explained that he couldn't be expected to do his work because the television 'distracted' his attention. As we pointed out, "If you walk past your school books, turn the television on, and sit down to enjoy the shows, it's not a 'distraction.' It's a bad choice."

Choices ADDers Often Make

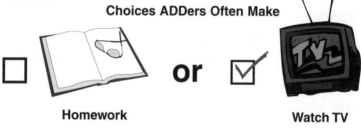

Homework   **Watch TV**

To further assist parents as they try to determine whether a behavior is deliberate or unconscious, track and document the problems. For instance, does the child forget to write down assignments in several classes or only in history? Does the child "lose" track of textbooks in every class, or is it only the math book which disappears regularly? Is the child impatient or temperamental with every member of the family, or only with parents?

2. Parents and ADD children should work together and develop a written list of specific **"behavioral expectations"** to serve as **"guidelines"** (terms which are much more "ADD friendly" than rules or laws) for good behavior.

Do not overwhelm the child with a lengthy list of expectations; work on **no more than two at a time**. Define the expectation and describe examples of what would constitute major and minor transgressions. In this way, it's easier to have the "punishment fit the crime" while calling attention to distinctions in degrees of behavior.

Next, the parents and the child should decide on appropriate consequences for **MAJOR** and **MINOR OFFENSES** as well as *"TREAT"* consequences for successfully meeting the expectations. A minor offense might result in a consequence such as, "Lose television privileges for tonight" while a major consequence might involve the loss of television privileges for a week or longer. *"TREAT"* slips might say, "You get to have your favorite food for dinner tomorrow" or give permission for an overnight guest on a weekend in the near future. *"TREATS"* are also available when the parent "catches" the child succeeding in a task or surpassing a goal independent of adult supervision. Treats don't have to be tied to a written contract; they can also be surprise rewards.

Write these consequences on color-coded slips of paper. For instance, minor consequences will be written on white paper, major ones on red slips, and "treats" in green. Then put all the slips into a large "jar of consequences."

When the child either commits an offense or earns a treat, he will reach into the jar and choose a slip to determine the outcome. By removing the parent from the role of being the "punishing force," the jar strategy reduces the level of personal conflict, and within the mind of the

Jar of Consequences

child, the connection between the behavior and consequence becomes more clear. (Few children will be able to say, "I'm being punished because the jar hates me!" and keep a straight face.)

Both the child and parent(s) sign the expectations paper. Copy the contract and give one copy to the child; post the other copy in a prominent spot, such as on the refrigerator or family message board.

Post the contract.

Sample:

Expectation: For the next two weeks, you will show respect for the property of others. You will do this by:

1. Not touching your father's desk or computer work area.
2. Wearing your own clothes; no "borrowing" from the closets of other family members.
3. Staying out of mother's work room.

MINOR offense example = Taking Dad's stapler from the desk and not returning it.

MAJOR offense example= Taking Dad's Cross pen from his desk and breaking or losing it.

Consequences: On the first minor offense, you will draw a minor consequence slip. On the second minor offense, you will draw a major consequence slip. Any major offenses will require a major consequence slip. If you have successfully met the expectations all week long, on Friday after dinner, you will draw a *"TREAT"* slip.

_____   _____
Parent(s) signature   Child's signature

At the end of the one or two week "trial period," the expectations and behavior performance should be reviewed, evaluated for effectiveness, and renewed or adjusted as necessary. **NOTE:** This strategy works best when proposed as a system for the entire family. In other words, the ADD child should not be "targeted" as the only family member with explicit expectations/ guidelines. If siblings and parents also post their obligations and track their performance records, the ADD child won't feel singled out as the "bad one," and the general concept of self-improvement will be presented in a more positive light.

3. After setting expectations for the child, **parents should prepare themselves for how they will react when the child fails to meet the expectations.** This sort of "preparation for the worst" may be disconcerting for some parents because it seems to clash with the rosy hopes they hold for the child's success. However, **mistakes are an inevitable part of the learning process**, and unless parents mentally rehearse their responses, they may overreact emotionally, turning what should be a lesson into a personal conflict which has no winners.

**Warning:
Danger Ahead**

When reacting to the child's mistake, parents must keep their focus on the problem and steer clear of personal recriminations and accusatory "you" judgments. Given the sensitive nature of ADD children, the ADD youngster will

AVOID "YOU" Judgements

hear only selected parts of what the parent says, filtering out much of the context and interpreting negative remarks automatically as personal attacks. By practicing what will be said before the problem occurs, parents will have better control over the situation. The sample comments below illustrate a "spur of the moment" spontaneous negative reaction; the bold type words are what the child hears selectively. Read the passage twice, but on the second reading, only note the bold type words.

Spontaneous response: "I can't believe **you deliberately** went into my desk, took my calculator, and **broke it**. Didn't you sign a contract which promised **you** wouldn't do something like this? Was that a **lie?** That calculator cost over $50! I guess **we can't trust you** around our stuff. Maybe we should lock up everything of value in the house so **you** won't **ruin everything**."

The message received by the child is clearly negative, particularly if the tone of voice communicates "shocked anger." However, if the adult consistently asserts that the criticism is directed at the behavior, not at the child, it will be easier to review the actual dynamics of the problem and make adjustments for better solutions.

Planned response: "Taking the calculator from my desk violated the expectation we set for this week. What do we expect from each other about respecting proper-ty?"(The child responds by stating the expectation. If he doesn't remember, show him the contract.) "Were you thinking about that when you walked toward the desk?" (The child will probably say,

Keep the contract handy when working with mistakes.

"No.") "What were you thinking about when you went to the desk?" (The child might say he was in a rush to finish his math assignment and couldn't find his own calculator; because he was in a hurry, he dropped the calculator and broke it.)

"It's very important that you don't repeat this behavior. Why do you think I would say that?" (The child's response may include "It makes you upset when I take your things," or "The calculator was expensive," etc.)

"We need to figure out a way for you to be reminded of the guidelines the next time you are tempted to take something from my desk. What would be a good reminder?" Help the child "brainstorm" possible reminders, such as having a special place for his own calculator, so it doesn't get lost, taping a copy of the guidelines on the desk drawer, or putting a red "sticker" on the parent's calculator.

Use visual reminders to help the ADDer remember the expectations.

"We'll see if the reminder helps next time, but you do need to draw a red slip from the consequence jar for not meeting the guideline this time."

4. Analyze the impact of environmental factors on the child's behaviors and alter circumstances when it's possible. For example, since ADD children are easily overstimulated by group

ADDers can become overstimulated in group activities.

situations, parents should observe their children to see how long it takes for them to become agitated. Using this guideline, parents should limit the amount of time spent at gatherings such as birthday parties or group picnics. (By the way, it's better to arrive late than to try to convince an ADD child to leave the party early!)

Altering the environment also includes

reducing the factors which will tempt the child to stray from established expectations. For instance, if the child is expected to complete her keyboarding practice before being allowed to play a favorite CD ROM game, remove the CD from the computer area until after the practice is completed. Or, if talking on the phone is the temptation, unplug and remove all phones within her view (leaving at least one plugged in wherever the parents can monitor its use).

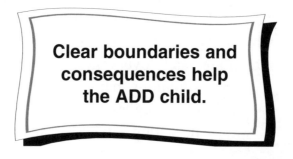

Clear boundaries and consequences help the ADD child.

Why Does An Active ADD Child Hate Gym Class?

Many ADD children lag behind their peers in terms of developing gross motor and/or fine motor skills, and this delayed development in some children often translates into a distaste for and an avoidance of athletics. (Gross motor skills use the larger muscle groups such as in soccer; fine motor skills involve the smaller muscle groups in the fingers, like handwriting.) Children in general will abandon an activity if they don't experience success; ADD children who traditionally lack perseverance will be even quicker to give up a task they perceive as hopeless. This surrender affects the student's physical

Gross motor skills can affect the development of social skills.

development because he will be less active, yet it also has an insidious effect on the child's social skills.

The playground is the arena where children learn to interact with their peers, to function as part of a group dynamic as well as an individual. Failure to "fit into the team" and the attendant feelings of rejection may evolve into bitterness and anti-social behaviors. However, if more time is devoted to working on fundamental motor skills during early childhood years, ADD children can become more confident of their abilities and less hesitant to "join the game."

Gross motor abilities are dependent upon basic skills such as balance and rhythm (as in walking, running, skipping), spatial awareness (going around objects instead of bumping into them), and response speed (quick reactions necessary for playing catch, batting, etc.). Without the adequate development of these gross motor "basics," the student's ability to execute fine motor activities (handwriting, typing, handling silverware) may be hampered. Teachers and parents who employ the following suggestions will perform a service which provides a lifetime of benefit for the ADD child.

Many ADDers struggle with fine motor skills.

1. Whenever introducing the ADD child to a motor skill activity, break the skill into small steps. For example, if the child can't coordinate his upper and lower body to jump rope successfully,

he should begin by learning to swing the rope rhythmically over the head, stepping over it instead of jumping. Next, he should practice jumping in rhythm without a rope involved. The final step is to combine the two actions.

2. When introducing an activity to a child, give verbal instructions while modeling the process. Trying merely to talk through the process without demonstrating the actions presents difficulties for ADD children who often have a hard time processing sequential information auditorially.

3. ADD children can easily become "couch potatoes" for life if they don't develop the habit of being active. At least four times a week, the child should engage in some form of physical activity, such as walking or riding bikes. Parents can encourage their offspring to participate in these healthy habits by accompanying the children on excursions around the neighborhood or in the park. These trips allow the parent and child to spend time together—not to mention the added benefit of providing the "grown up" with some regular exercise! ADD

children often have an affinity for animals. Taking a dog for a walk on a daily basis is another way to make being active more palatable.

4. Many fine motor skills require a person to use both sides of the body in harmony; this ability is called bilateral coordination. For example, using scissors to cut paper involves employing the non-dominant hand to hold the paper in conjunction with the action of the dominant hand which works the scissors.

A child with poor bilateral coordination cannot successfully cut in a straight line because he forgets to move his non-dominant hand while cutting. One method to improve this fine motor skill is to have the child practice cutting straight lines on a piece of paper marked with a series of dots to designate where the non-dominant hand should hold the paper. As the child moves the cutting edge of the scissors forward, he advances the other hand to the next dot. This practice should be monitored at first, for even with the dots to follow, some children forget to move their hands. Gentle reminders to "move to the next dot" may be needed until the

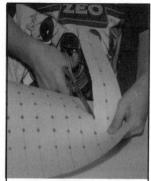

Cutting paper requires both hands to work in a rhythm.

ADDer "gets into sync" with the process.

Writing is another fine motor skill which requires bilateral coordination; however, the work of the non-dominant is often overlooked because of the attention focused on the hand holding the pencil. As children practice writing, parents and teachers should monitor the position of the non-dominant hand and make sure it is used to "anchor" the paper in place during the exercise.

Writing requires the use of two hands.

Does Traveling In A Car With An ADD Child Have To Be Disasterous?

Hyperactive children who have no concept of time are not the best companions for long trips in the confined space of an automobile, to say the least! Despite patient explanations that the trip to grandmother's house will take more than five hours, the children will probably start asking "Are we there yet?" five minutes after leaving the driveway. Moreover, restless behavior which is barely tolerable within the space of a house or yard quickly becomes a nightmare when it occurs within the confines of the back seat. In truth, the antics of an ADD child during a car trip can become a safety concern because the driver of the vehicle is unable to give full attention to the highway. Wise parents will take advantage of the following tips to make driving vacations both safer and more relaxing.

Are we there yet?

1. Take a small travel clock on the trip. (An analog style timepiece is  the best choice.) Show the child where the hands of the clock will be at departure time and where they will be when they arrive. Help the child determine how many hours the trip should take. If the child doesn't have

Use a clock on a trip to teach time estimation.

a clear understanding of how long an hour is, explain it in terms of something familiar: "It's two episodes of The Mighty Morphin Power Rangers (or whatever the child's favorite television show may be)."

Set the alarm to ring at the approximate mid-point of the journey to signal "halfway there." When this alarm sounds, reset it to signal "three-fourths of the way there."

2. Make a photocopy of the map and high-light the route of the trip. As the journey proceeds, the child can track the family's progress through towns and cities along the way, a process which also offers practice in directionality and map-read-ing skills. Parents can even

Make a road trip an active learning time.

turn this tactic into a time estimation game by asking the child to guess how long it will take to reach the next town. The child can use a stop watch to test the estimate. Carry a compass and regularly ask which direction the car is pointing. Pass out change to be spent at the next stop for correctly reading signs on the highway.

3. Pack a box of diversions. Fill it with comic books, snacks, puzzles, and travel games. Parents should then "dole" these amusements out to the child at intervals. Under no circumstances should the child be given the entire box at the start of the trip. The child will spend thirty minutes rifling through the contents and then complain of boredom for the next four and a half hours! In any case, these treats will be more fun as a series of surprises.

Bring a box of surprises on the trip.

4. If more than one child is on the trip, assign seats in the car and rotate the seating arrangement at regular intervals.

5. Plan frequent breaks whether going on a vacation or an all-day shopping expedition. In a car trip, there should be a short break to "stretch

the legs" about every hour or so, depending on the age of the child. At the mall, plan to get a snack or visit a play area between every store; establishing a "shopping schedule" which lists the stores makes it easier to set the "break times."

How Can "Physical Restlessness" Be A Positive Factor In Learning?

The high level of physical restlessness common to hyperactive ADDers can be channeled constructively to help them develop memory skills. Many ADD children are kinesthetic learners, meaning they learn through motion, and memory for motor skills activities are typically very strong for all people. For example, once someone learns to drive a car, the knowledge becomes a permanent part of the person's long-term memory. In addition, movement demands active involvement, and it also helps focus attention. Incorporating music and rhythm into motor skill activities makes them more appealing to ADD children as well.

1. Draw large circles, squares, triangles and rectangles on the sidewalk using colored chalk. The student is then given oral instructions, such as "Walk forward until you reach the yellow triangle; then turn left and walk to the blue square." Children can work on listening skills and directionality simultaneously with this exercise.

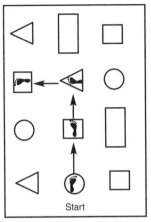

Incorporate listening and directionality training into the same activity.

2. When learning to divide words into syllables, the child should tap the table for each syllable, stand up/sit down for each syllable, or feel the chin drop for each new syllable.

Math facts are more fun on a trampoline.

3. The child should try jumping on a mini-trampoline while counting aloud by 2's, 3's, and so on.

4. Teach the child dances such as the "Hokey-Pokey" or the Macarena to practice following directions and remembering sequences.

5. Jumping ropes while reciting poems helps a student become more conscious of the rhythm of the poetry.

6. Have children hop on an alphabet mat while singing their ABC's. The motor movement slows them down so they can concentrate on the letter's look as well as its name. This tactic will help clear up the confusion children often have about the "L-M-N-O-P" sequence; many of them believe the sequence is a single letter ("Elemenope") because they rush through that part of the song so fast.

```
 N  Y  X  W  V  U  T  S  R  Q  P  O  N
 A  B  C  D  E  F  G  H  I  J  K  L  M
START
```

7. Hopping back and forth on number lines makes addition and subtraction easier for some children to understand. This same technique can be used for positive and negative numbers.

```
-10 -9 -8 -7 -6 -5 -4 -3 -2 -1 0 1 2 3 4 5 6 7 8 9 10
```

8. Introduce the concept of one-to-one correspondence by playing musical chairs.

How Can Teacher's Accommodate The Hyper Child In The Classroom?

Children with ADD have "energy to burn," and sitting passively at desks for longer than ten or fifteen minutes at a stretch is almost physically impossible for them. Wise teachers provide outlets for the diversion of this extra energy into more productive channels.

1. Plan "stand up and stretch" breaks every half hour or so. Such breaks are also beneficial before and after testing situations.

Plan stretch breaks.

2. On warm, sunny days, obtain permission to take the class outside for brief "observation walks." Upon returning to class, have the students list the details of what they saw, heard, smelled, and felt during the walk.

3. The ADD child makes a great "teacher's helper" for passing out and picking up materials.

The ADDer can be a teacher's helper.

Many of these children love working with their hands and enjoy performing tasks such as running film strip projectors or working on computers; however, make sure the "helper" demonstrates how to operate the equipment prior to class time.

4. Train the ADD child to be the class "errand runner." Time how long it should take him to reach various locations (main office, library, nurse's office, etc.) if walking at a moderate pace and establish a "target time" for these errands. The student's goal is to accomplish the errand within the time frame, which means "no running" and "no dawdling." As long as the target time is met, the child keeps the errand runner "job."

5. If the child disturbs classmates by tapping his pencil or fingers, allow him to "fidget" with quieter materials, such as squeezing therapy putty or a small rubber ball—as long as the materials stay on the student's desk. ADD students can often do a better job of listening and concentrating when "fiddling" with objects; permitting the child to do so

should be conditional on whether he is able to focus on the lesson at hand and respond to questions. (The same principle applies to "doodling" in the margins of notebooks.)

6. Children with "oral fixations" who constantly chew on pencils or rubber erasers could be allowed to chew sugar-free gum—as long as it stays in their mouths! The privilege is rescinded for one week if the gum isn't properly disposed by being wrapped in paper and placed in the trash.

7. Establish a "walkabout" area in the back of the class for the child who "paces while think-

Create casual reading centers.

e classrooms have incorporated ual areas" for reading or studying which contain bean bag chairs, pillows, or even a rocking chair. These areas are great for ADDers who have to "sprawl out" to study more efficiently.

8. Have children move to new chairs (or desk groups) when switching subjects, such as going from math practice to social studies map work. Such variety not only gives them a physical change, it also allows them to "move mentally" and prepare for different tasks.

When one of our ADD clients made the jump from elementary to junior high, he was extremely enthusiastic about his new school. What did he like best? "Every hour or so, we get to get up and walk through the halls before we start something new. It's COOL!"

Physically moving between subjects or classes helps the ADDer become less fidgety.

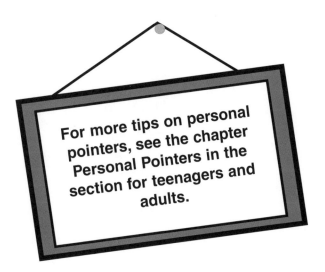

For more tips on personal pointers, see the chapter Personal Pointers in the section for teenagers and adults.

Appendix

ADD STATISTICS

1. According to statistics, there are 1 to 3 ADD students in every classroom of thirty students.
2. 3 to 6 more boys are diagnosed than girls.
3. ADD children develop emotionally at 30% slower rate than non-ADD peers; for example, an ADD child of 10 operates at the maturity level of a 7 year old; a teenage driver of 16 is age 11 in decision making skills. Teachers and parents should adjust their expectations accordingly.
4. 65% of ADD youngsters have problems with stubbornness, defiance, refusal to obey, temper tantrums, and verbal hostility.
5. 25% of ADD students have serious learning problems in one or more of these areas: oral expression, listening comprehension, written expression, basic reading skills, reading comprehension, mathematical calculation, and mathematical reasoning.
6. 50% of ADD students have listening comprehension problems.
7. 1/3 of all ADD students have one or more of these learning problems:
    1. Language deficits (poor listening comprehension, poor verbal expression, poor reading comprehension)
    2. Poor organizational skills
    3. Poor memory
    4. Poor fine motor skills.
8. 1/3 to 1/2 of students who have ADD have problems with expressive language. (This is two or three times the rate for students without ADD.)
9. Nearly half of hyper ADD children are accident-prone; 15% have had serious accidents.

10. 75% of the boys with ADD are hyperactive; 60% of the girls are hyperactive

11. 40% of all youngsters with ADD have at least one parent who has ADD.

12. Neither sugar nor artificial sweeteners causes hyper-activity; however, about 3% of ADDers may react to food allergies.

13. 50% of ADD children have sleep disorders.

14. Parents of ADD children are three times as likely to separate or divorce as parents of non–ADD children.

15. Children with ADD who live in a single-parent family have more problems with aggression than ADD children living with a two-parent family.

16. Ritalin has been found effective with approximately 70% - 80% of children with ADHD.

17. Stimulant medication is less effective with those who have ADD without hyperactivity.

18. Ritalin has been carefully studied for over 25 years and has been proven safe for long-term use.

19. Children with ADD need positive feedback more often than other children do; ideally they should receive 3 compliments for every negative comment.

20. Length of "time out" should be 1 minute for every year of age i.e. 8 minutes for an 8 year old.

21. 50% of children with ADD have poor motor coordination.

22. ADD children without hyperactivity are more likely to become depressed than those with hyperactivity.

23. ADHD alone does not appear to put a teenager at risk for drug use; however, ADHD in combination with high levels of aggression and hyperactivity does.

24. Predictors of future substance abuse: a. Associating with those who use drugs. b. Being aggressive and hyperactive.

25. Teenagers with ADHD have almost four times as many traffic citations as non-ADHD teens; speeding is the most frequent citation.

26. Teens with ADHD have four times as many car wrecks and are more than seven times as likely to have a second accident. They are four times as likely to be at fault in the accident.

27. 21% of ADD teens skip school repeatedly.

28. 35% of ADD teens drop out of school.

29. 45% of ADD teens have been suspended.

30. 30% of ADHD and ADD without hyperactivity have failed a year of school.

31. 1/3 - 1/2 of youngsters with ADHD have chronic health problems such as upper respiratory infections, allergies, and asthma.

32. The number of children with ADHD is conservatively placed at 3 - 5%, or one in every 25 to 30 children.* This estimate means over 2 million children in the United States have ADHD. The number of children currently being treated with Ritalin ranges from 750,000 to 1.6 million, depending on which study is cited. Based on these numbers, we are not over medicating children with ritalin. (*Some experts feel this percentage is too low, and they estimate the figures could go as high as 8 to 13%.)

33. When properly administered, stimulant medications have a positive effect on ADHD behavior. Youths placed on therapeutic medication are better able to cope with the pressures of growing up and may be less likely to turn to illegal drugs.

Information adapted from Russell Barkley, Ph.D.
University of Massachusetts Medical School

ADD Quick Tips

7 Steps
To
Successful
Writing

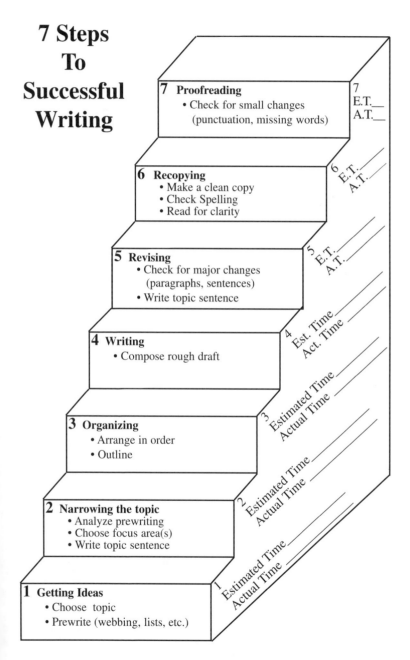

7 Proofreading
• Check for small changes
  (punctuation, missing words)

7
E.T.__
A.T.__

6 Recopying
• Make a clean copy
• Check Spelling
• Read for clarity

6
E.T.__
A.T.__

5 Revising
• Check for major changes
  (paragraphs, sentences)
• Write topic sentence

5
E.T.__
A.T.__

4 Writing
• Compose rough draft

4
Est. Time __
Act. Time __

3 Organizing
• Arrange in order
• Outline

3
Estimated Time __
Actual Time __

2 Narrowing the topic
• Analyze prewriting
• Choose focus area(s)
• Write topic sentence

2
Estimated Time __
Actual Time __

1 Getting Ideas
• Choose topic
• Prewrite (webbing, lists, etc.)

1
Estimated Time __
Actual Time __

Behavior Scale for Medication

Name: _____ Grade: _____

Date: _____ School: _____

Completed by: _____ Physician: _____

Days Needed for Feedback: 1   2   3   4   5

This form is being used to determine the effectiveness of medication.

Check any changes in behavior.

BEHAVIORS	9:00 am	10:00am	11:00am	12 noon	1:00 pm	2:00 pm	3:00 pm
Fidgety, restless							
Excessive talking							
Blurts out in class							
Problems staying on task							
Problems listening							
Not following directions							
Appears disorganized							
Impulsive							
Aggressive/rude							

Comments

_____

_____

_____

_____

Have the child's teacher or teachers fill out this form daily, so the effectiveness of the medicine can be tracked. The physician can make a more informed decision about medication issues if the person can see a pattern of when the medicine is and isn't effective.

ADD Quick Tips, Brainworks, Inc., 1918 Walnut Plaza, Carrollton, Texas 75006, (972) 416-9410

Rules For Home

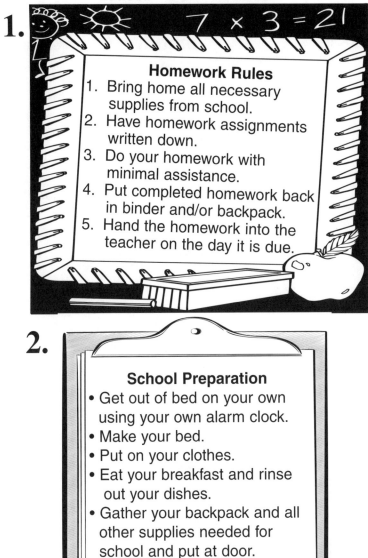

1.

Homework Rules
1. Bring home all necessary supplies from school.
2. Have homework assignments written down.
3. Do your homework with minimal assistance.
4. Put completed homework back in binder and/or backpack.
5. Hand the homework into the teacher on the day it is due.

2.

School Preparation
- Get out of bed on your own using your own alarm clock.
- Make your bed.
- Put on your clothes.
- Eat your breakfast and rinse out your dishes.
- Gather your backpack and all other supplies needed for school and put at door.

Rules should be posted for ADD students, so there is no misunderstanding about the expectations.

3.

Laundry Rules

- Take laundry to your room.
- Hang up anything that should be hung up. (pants, blouses, dresses)
- Put the rest of the clothes (underwear, socks, t-shirts) in the correct drawer.
- Don't crumple up the clothes or stuff too much into each drawer.

4.

PERSONAL POSSESSIONS

- Get a basket or wagon and go through the house gathering all of your toys, books, etc.

- Sort the items.

- Put in the appropriate places.

Don't throw everything under the bed or in the closet!

ADD Quick Tips

5.

Supper Rules

- Be on time.
- No yelling or food fights.
- Ask politely for any food out of your reach.
- Chew with your mouth closed.
- Respond to questions.
- Keep your voice volume down.

6.

Kitchen Cleanup Rules

- Put items that belong in the refrigerator up first.
- Scrape the uneaten food into the garbage disposal.
- Make a sink of warm, sudsy water.
- Rinse or wash the dishes.
- Put the dishes in the dishwasher.
- Add detergent.
- When the dishwasher has stopped, put dishes up in the cabinet.

7.

Bedroom Chores

1. Pick up all of the toys and put in bins and/or toybox.
2. Put clean clothes into the drawers or hang in the closet.
3. Put dirty clothes into the laundry hamper.
4. Throw away all trash.
5. Make your bed. Fold the blanket if the bed is already made.
6. Clean off all counterspace (dresser, desk, etc.).
7. Dust all the wood on the bed, dresser, desk, etc.
8. Vacuum or sweep the floor.

8.

CHORES
Daily

	Mon	Tues	Wed	Thurs	Fri	Sat	Sun
1. Be ready for school on time.							
2. Clean your bedroom.							
3. Put up personal possessions.							
4. Put up your own laundry.							
5. Be on time for supper and follow the rules.							
6. Do the dishes.							
7. Do your homework.							
8. Be ready for bed on time.							

Weekly

	Mon	Tues	Wed	Thurs	Fri	Sat	Sun
1. Take out the trash.							
2. Mow the yard.							
3. Rake leaves or pull weeds.							
4. Bathe the dog.							

Extra (Bonus Privileges)

	Mon	Tues	Wed	Thurs	Fri	Sat	Sun
1. Clean the bathroom.							
2. Sweep and mop the kitchen.							
3. Vacuum the living room.							
4. Clean out the car.							
5. Read for 30 minutes.							
6.							
7.							

Post a weekly chart on the refrigerator or bulletin board that lists daily and weekly chores.

JOINT - FAMILY RESPONSIBILITIES

9.

Chores	Mon	Tue	Wed	Thur	Fri	Sat	Sun
1. **Vacuum & Dust Bedroom**							
2. **Vacuum & Dust Living Room**							
3. **Bathroom Duty**							
4. **Take Out Trash**							
5. **Set The Table**							
6. **Load Dishwasher**							
7. **Cook**							
8. **Wash, Dry, & Fold Clothes**							
9. **Press (Iron) Clothes**							
10. **Feed Pets & Pet Care**							
11. **Make Bed & Pick Up Room**							
12. **Yard Work**							

To Be Considered:

1. Which responsibilities are expected everyday? weekly?
2. What is the expected completion time?
3. What happens if the responsibility is not completed on time?
4. Which responsibilities can be selected for monthly or weekly rotation?
5. How is it handled if something unexpected happens and prevents the person from fulfilling the responsibility?
6. Is the task appropriate for the age of the family member?

A family calendar for chores may be easier than having an individual chart for each family member.

Assignment Sheet

Name _____

Date _____

SUBJECT	MON	TUES	WED	THURS	FRI
Language Arts 					
Social Studies 					
Math 					
Science 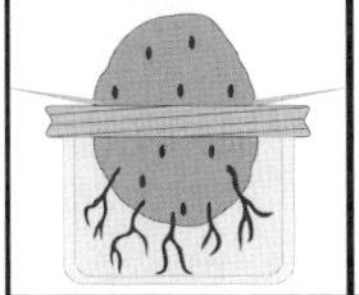					
Other_____ 					
Long-Term Dates					

One assignment sheet for all subjects is much better for ADD Students.

Sunday	Monday	Tuesday	Wednesday	Thursday	Friday	Saturday
Long-Term Projects - Due In February 1. Book Report on Biography Due Feb. 21st 2. Science Fair Project Due Feb. 26th 3. Social Studies - Group Presentation on Indian Culture Feb.28th						**1** Go to the library and choose a book on Indians, a biography, and a book on Science Fair Projects.
2	**3** Read biography. Write short summary after each chapter.	**4** Read biography. Write chapter summary.	**5** Read biography. Write chapter summary.	**6** Read biography. Write chapter summary.	**7** Read biography. Write chapter summary.	**8** Look through Science books and choose a project. Buy posterboard.
9	**10** Decide in Social Studies group what each individual's assignment is.	**11** Read biography. Write chapter summary.	**12** Finish reading biography and read through Science experiment.	**13** Write book report rough draft. Assemble ingredients for science fair project.	**14** Do Science Fair Experiment. Write Results. Take pictures.	**15** Write Science Fair results neatly and put pictures and results neatly on presentation board.
16	**17** Read information about Indians for Social Studies.	**18** Make a rough draft of Social Studies project.	**19** Read through book report rough draft and write neatly for final copy.	**20** Check to make sure book report is in backpack for school tomorrow.	**21** BOOK REPORT DUE	**22** Write Indian project neatly and make related posterboard for presentation.
23	**24** Do last minute changes for Science Fair and/or Social Studies Projects.	**25** Put Science Fair Project by front door for tomorrow.	**26** SCIENCE FAIR PROJECT DUE	**27** Meet with Social Studies group and make sure everyone has done their part.	**28** SOCIAL STUDIES INDIANS FINAL PROJECT	

Scheduling multiple assignments can be difficult for ADD students. Learning to plan long-term is an essential lifeskill. The secret is shorter daily deadlines; the teacher must see evidence of work in progress each day.

Time Management Calender

Name_____ Date_____ Class_____

Times	MON.	TUES.	WED.	THURS.	FRI.	SAT.	SUN.
3:00-3:30	School	School	School				
3:30-4:00	Snack Chores	Snack Chores	Snack Chores				
4:00-4:30	Piano Practice	Study	Study				
4:30-5:00	Drive ↑	Drive ↑	Free Time				
5:00-5:30	Math Tutor	Soccer					
5:30-6:00	↓ Drive	↓ Drive	↓				
6:00-6:30	Free Time	Study	Eat				
6:30-7:00	Eat	Eat	Chores				
7:00-7:30	Chores	Chores	Study				
7:30-8:00	TV	Study	TV				
8:00-8:30	TV	TV	Study				
8:30-9:00	Study	Free Time	Free Time				
9:00-9:30							
9:30-10:00	↓	↓	↓				
10:00-10:30	Bed	Bed	Bed				
10:30-11:00							
11:00-11:30							
11:30-12:00	↓	↓	↓				
Fun/Free Time	1hr. 30min.	2 hrs.	3hr. 30min.				

Document free time first when teaching scheduling.

Appendix of Alphabet Letters

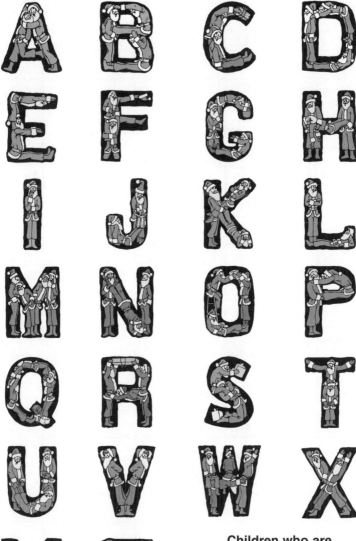

Children who are
kinesthetic learners may
memorize the letters easier
if they form the letters on
the floor.

"COPS" CHECKLIST

Before handing in the composition, "police the paper" by checking the following areas:

C = Capitalization
LOOK for capital letters in these places:
_____ 1. The first letter of the first word in each sentence
_____ 2. The first letter of proper nouns (names of people, months and days, states, cities, streets, holidays)
_____ 3. The title of the composition

O = Overall appearance
LOOK at the paper. Did you:
_____ 1. Indent the first line of each paragraph?
_____ 2. Stay within the left and right margins?
_____ 3. Write neatly? Make corrections by drawing a single line through the mistake, writing the correction above?

P = Punctuation
LOOK at punctuation marks. Did you:
_____ 1. Use correct punctuation (periods, question marks, exclamation points) at the end of each sentence?
_____ 2. Use commas for:
       Dates (January 31, 1955)
       City and state (Dallas, Texas)
       Items in a series (She loves toys, games, and dogs.)
       Introductory clauses (When I finish the job, I'll go home.)
       Joining 2 independent clauses
       (She made the cake, but I ate it.)
_____ 3. Use apostrophes with
       Contractions (won't, can't, I'll)
       Possession (Bob's bike, boys' bikes)

S = Spelling
LOOK for misspelled words. Did you:
_____ 1. Exchange papers with a classmate to check?
_____ 2. Circle words you think might be misspelled?
_____ 3. Use a dictionary or word list to check spellings?

References

Ayres, A.Jean. *Sensory Integration and Learning Disorders*.
  California: Western Psychological Services, 1972.
Barkley, Russell A. *Taking Charge of ADHD*. New York: The
  Guilford Press, 1995.
Baratta-Lorton, Mary. *Mathematics Their Way*. California: Addison-
  Wesley Publishing Company, 1976.
Burns, Marilyn. *About Teaching Mathematics*. Sausalito, California:
  Math Solutions Publication, 1992.
Clark, Lynn. *SOS-Help For Parents*. Kentucky: Parents Press, 1996.
Crutsinger, Carla. *Creative Memory*. Carrollton, Texas: Brainworks,
  1994.
Crutsinger, Carla. *Teenage Connection*. Carrollton, Texas.
  Brainworks, 1987.
Crutsinger, Carla. *Thinking Smarter*. Carrollton, Texas: Brainworks,
  1992.
Dendy, Chris A. Zeigler. *Teenagers with ADD - A Parent's Guide*.
  Maryland: Woodbine House, Inc., 1995.
Goldstein, Dr. Sam and Dr. Michael Goldstein. *Hyperactivity - Why
  Won't My Child Pay Attention?* John Wiley and Sons, Inc., 1992.
Hallowell, Edward M. and John J. Ratey. *Answers to Distraction*.
  New York: Pantheon Books, 1994.
Hallowell, Edward M. and John J. Ratey. *Driven to Distraction*. New
  York: Pantheon Books, 1994.
Mercer, Cecil D. and Ann R. Mercer. *Teaching Students with
  Learning Problems*. Canada: MacMillan Publishing Company,
  1993.
Quinn, Patricia. *Putting on the Brakes*. New York: Imagination
  Press, 1993.
Richardson, Kathy. *Developing Number Concepts Using Unifix®
  Cubes*. California: Addison-Wesley Publishing Company, 1984.
Rief, Sandra F. *How to Reach and Teach ADD/ADHD Children*. New
  York: The Center for Applied Research In Education, 1993.
Taylor, John. *Helping Your Hyperactive Child*. California: Prima
  Publishing and Communications, 1990.
Taylor, John. *"Answers to ADD: The School Success Tool Kit"*
  Video.

Index

A

active learning, 116, 299
ADD
- friendly, 10, 26-27, 40-41, 91, 175-178, 182, 285
- characteristics, 10, 86, 180
- relationship obstacles, 180
- the term, 181
- disorder of consistency, 73
- diet pyramid, 138
- training, 60-64
- careers, 176-178
- coach, 60-64
all or nothing, 66, 208
allergies, 137, 139-140
alligator zone, 253-254
answering machine, 31
anticipation, skill of, 60
assets, 172-173
assignment sheets, 26-28
attention, overabundance of, 181
auditory cues, 30-32, 186, 217
auditory processing, 106-107
Ayres, Jean, 247

B

back-ups, 30, 32, 62
back pack/bookbag, 37-39, 101, 107, 214, 216-217, 276
balanced reading program, 223-224
Baratta-Lorton, Mary, 235
battles, 23, 243
beat the clock, 225
bed, 25, 32-33, 145-154, 202, 205, 215
behavior pattern, 10, 48, 280-292
behavioral expectations, 280-292
bilateral coordination, 296-297
biographies, 175, 278
block schedules, 38
body language, 185-186

book organization, 35-36
boredom, 87-88, 99, 151,187, 225-226, 300
boundaries, 292
brainstorming, 127-130, 261-262, 264
breakfast, 141-144, 266
bulletin board, 24, 39
Burns, Marilyn, 235

C

caffeine, 138-139
calendar, 33, 41, 52-55, 57-60, 80-81, 206-208
 - week at a glance, 41, 58, 206
 - a day at a time, 52-53
 - family, 35, 54-55
 - day time planner, 33, 57-58
 - pocket size, 41, 58
calls, 31-32, 63
careers, 176-178
carrels, study, 97, 266
checklists, 159, 183-184, 199, 203-204, 263
cheese, 138-141, 143-144
class notes, 64, 100, 106, 113-114, 121-123, 164, 249
classroom modifications, 72-73, 79, 102, 144
clocks, 31, 49-50, 53-54, 91, 147, 209-211, 215-216, 225-226, 259, 299
coach, ADD, 60-64
color coding, 39, 58-59, 121, 236, 286
comparison of siblings, 276
communication, 108, 179, 181, 185, 187, 189
composition skills, 126-131, 261-267
concentration zone, 266
consequences, 75, 145, 168, 285-292
contract, 251, 285-292
conversation training, 184-185
couch potatoes, 295-296
Creative Memory, 117
creativity, 9, 27, 86, 116, 172
cure, 14, 165-166, 168, 199

D

daydreams, 88, 114
deadlines, 50, 72-81, 127
 - extending, 72-74
 - late work, 72, 77-78
deficiencies, 6, 9-10, 172-173, 277-278
denial, 56, 197-198
depression, 85-86, 135
design, study area, 87, 89-92, 94
desks, 21-25, 33-36, 41, 52, 89, 94, 96-100, 145, 174, 201, 246, 260,
         287, 289-91, 305-307
 - clustered, 97
 - solo, 97
 - study carrels, 97, 266
 - privileged seat, 99-100
diet, 138-144
directionality, 232, 240, 258-260, 299, 303
disorder of desperation, 9
distraction-free zone, 25, 87-88, 201
distractions, 25, 53, 87-94, 96-98, 106, 163, 180, 201, 284
documenting problems, 284
dry-erase board, 32, 54
dyslexia, 228

E

emotional age, 200
emotional maturity, 200, 273-274
empowered, 10
essays, 78, 124, 126-127
expectations, 15, 96, 168, 199-200, 221, 283, 285-288, 290-292
eye contact, 109-110, 187-188

F

failure, 9, 47, 67, 70, 72, 78, 99-101, 117, 145, 148, 168-169,
         184-185, 198, 232, 252, 271, 273, 275, 277, 283, 288
fast foods, 141-142
fear, 50, 163, 263, 271-272
fill-in-the-blank, 123-124, 130

fine motor skills, 243, 248-254, 293-294, 296-297, 302
flash cards, 117-120, 229
flexible planning, 54, 60, 207
free spirit, 50
free time, 54, 66-67, 206, 209
friendship qualities, 182

G

genius, 277
Goldstein, Michael, 281
Goldstein, Sam, 73, 244, 281
"goof-off" time, 207
grading, 12, 65, 70-71, 74-75, 78, 100-101, 103-105, 126-127,
        131, 135, 161, 165, 172-174, 220
gross motor skills, 273-274, 293-297, 302-308
guidelines, behavior, 285
gym class, 293-297

H

Hallowell, Edward, 9
handwriting problems, 73, 107, 118, 236, 248, 252, 256, 294
health issues, 135-167
 - diet, 138-144
hearing problems, 229
homework, 10, 25, 28-29, 31, 35-36, 38, 47, 55, 59, 65-71, 80,
        88-89, 91, 102, 104-105, 162-163, 165, 168, 176, 201,
        208-209, 217, 236-237, 241, 249, 256, 283-284
 - pocket folder, 28-29, 31, 41-42, 58
 - muscles, 65-66
 - purpose, 67, 69, 90, 99
 - "homework cop", 68
 - marathons, 68
 - time by grade level, 68
 - grades, 65, 70, 76-78, 100-101, 104-105, 127, 131
 - stalling, 71
 - in-class time, 69, 77, 95, 99, 148
 - adjustments, 60, 81, 95, 99, 200
 - hand reminders, 30-31
 - headings, 36, 103

hyperactivity, 114, 139-140, 302

I

identification questions, 123
incompetence, 281-283
individualized reading instruction, 226
infections, 137, 229
inner clock, 49

J

K

kinesthetic learner, 230-231, 302-304

L

labeling, 163, 172, 180, 228, 276-277
laziness, 170-172
learn by endurance, 114-115
learning process, 288
learning style, 86, 183, 230-231
letter recall, 257-258, 260
lifestyle of failure, 73, 283
lighting, 93-94
listening, 86, 88 93, 106-112, 164, 179, 181, 184, 186, 240,
        252, 274, 303, 306
lockers, 35, 36, 174
"lone wolf", 181-182, 273-274
long-term assignments, 80, 127-128
look over information, 113-115
lunch, 141-144, 159, 204, 276

M

management, 10-11, 13, 48-49, 126, 135-136, 145, 151, 165,
        179, 195, 206, 281
map-reading skills, 212, 299, 307
margins, 255, 307
math, 14, 27, 67, 93, 105, 107, 159, 176, 210, 232-241

- games, 232-235
- manipulatives, 235
- signs, 236
- columns, 236-237, 241
- errors, 238
medication, 31, 48, 139, 142, 144, 155-167, 211
- time management, 48-49, 126, 136, 158-164, 195, 206
- teenagers, 57, 93, 163-164, 169, 175, 185-186
- weird feeling, 164
memory, 69, 93, 107, 114, 117, 123, 223, 231, 234-235, 238, 243, 258-260, 302
Mercer, Ann, 224, 263
Mercer, Cecil D., 224, 263
mindmapping, 262
multiple choice tests, 123-124
mnemonics, 238
modifications, 72-73, 79, 102, 135, 144, 166
motivation, 7, 34, 135, 168-178, 182, 271-279
motor skills, 243, 248-254, 273-274, 293-297, 302-308

N

National Center for Learning Disabilities, 227
National Institute of Mental Health, 137
noise, 42, 87-89, 91-93, 221-222
noncompliance, 281-292
non-dominant hand, 231, 254, 296-297
non-verbal communication, 185-187, 189
non-verbal cues, 109, 185-186, 265
note of praise, 274-276
notebook grades, 100
note taking, 64, 106, 113-114, 121-123, 164, 249
nutrition, 137, 142

O

obstacles, social, 180-182
offenses (major and minor), 285-287
organization, 7, 9, 21-42, 100, 126, 128, 136, 195-217
organizer supplies, 40-42
organizers, 22-23, 36, 40
out of sight, 22

overstimulation, 149-150

P

pain, 175, 248-255
paper angle, 253-255
passive learning, 113, 115-116
past, present, and future, 49
pencil grasp, 247-254
permanent fix, 13, 166
personal pointers, 135-189, 269-308
 - health issues, 135-167
 - diet, 138-144
 - sleep, 137, 140, 145-154
 - medication, 31, 48, 137, 139-140, 142, 144, 155-167, 211
piles, 21-24
pill dispensers, 211
Post-its®, 33-34, 41, 70, 173-174
 - placement, 33-34, 70, 173
problem-solving questions, 196, 198, 282
problem child personality, 281
procrastination, 65-71, 73, 198, 208
proofreading, 130-131, 244, 261, 263

Q

Quick Tip guidelines, 12-15

R

reading program, 223-231
reading speed, 229
rebellion, 56
relaxation, 149-152
reminders, 24, 30-32, 59, 173-174, 291, 296
rescuing, 195-196
research papers, 126
restlessness, 180, 302-308
review, 13, 70, 95, 98, 105, 113, 120-121, 123-124, 129-131,
        161, 173-174, 189, 199, 226, 233, 245, 290
rewrite options, 131, 263
Richardson, Kathy, 235

role model, 179
rough draft, 130, 262-263

S

seating arrangement, 95-99, 300
self-awareness, 183
self-esteem, 9, 48, 79, 85, 135-136, 145, 166-167, 169, 171,
        174-175, 228, 271-279
sense of time, 37, 47
sequencing, 104, 106-108, 145, 149, 205, 238, 243-244, 267, 303
short bursts, 29, 68, 79, 102
sight word vocabulary, 229-230
sleep patterns, 137, 140, 145-154, 213
snacks, 90, 143-144
social skills, 179-189, 293
  - body language, 185-186
  - checklists, 183-184, 199, 203-204
  - conversation training, 184-185
  - eye contact, 109-110, 187-188
  - friendship qualities, 182
  - "lone wolf", 181-182, 273-274
  - non-verbal communication, 185-187, 189
  - obstacles, 180-182
  - self-awareness, 10, 183, 195
  - tone of voice, 186-187, 189, 289
solutions, 9-10, 235, 290
space issues, 195-205
spatial cues, 22, 210, 274, 294
sports, 111, 273-274
sterile and boring, 21
stimulant medication, 144, 155-167
stopwatch, 41, 211, 216, 226, 300
stress management, 135, 151-152
strengths, 6, 10, 172, 230, 276-278
stretch breaks, 305
study buddy, 29, 98, 124, 173
study log, 102
study strategies, 85-131, 219-267
sugar, 138-140, 143
supplies to avoid, 40-42

syllables, 303

T

tactile cues, 30-31, 231
tactile learners, 231
tape recorders, 189, 264
task oriented, 50
Taylor, John, 106
Teenage Connection, 186-188
teflon students, 244
test taking, 26, 70, 105, 123-124, 160, 172, 196, 300
tests and preparation, 115-125
textbooks, 70, 85, 100-103, 113, 123
therapy putty, 251, 306-307
Thinking Smarter, 117
three second rule, 117-120
three times rule, 121-125
time awareness, 47, 66, 79, 195, 206-217
time estimation, 62-63, 81, 102, 126, 129, 299
time management, 48-49, 126, 136, 195, 206-212
time tips, 45-81, 195-217
time training, 52-55, 215-217
timer, 217
tone of voice, 186-187, 189, 289
tracking problems, 12, 283
traveling, 212, 298-301
true/false questions, 123-124

U

unconditional love, 279
untimed tests, 79
upper body strength, 243, 247-248

V

visual cues, 22, 30, 32, 52, 59, 173-174, 203, 209, 291
visual distractions, 94, 97
visual problems, 228-229, 243
visual stimuli, 22, 38, 87
visual thinker, 21-23, 117, 121, 129, 235

visualizing, 108-109, 152, 231
voice cues, 186

W

walkabout, 307
walk-in closet, 25, 90
watches, 49-50, 53-54
 - analog, 53, 209-210
 - digital, 53, 209-210
 - novelty, 210-211
webbing, 121-123, 262
weird feeling, 164
white noise, 91-93
word processing, 255
writing partners, 130, 131
writing, process, 126-131, 243-245, 261, 264
writing skills, 126-131, 243-245, 257-260
 - handwriting, 73, 107, 118, 131, 236, 248-254, 256-261
 - composition, 126-131, 261-267

Y

"yes...but", 274-275
yes/no questions, 111-112
you judgments, 288-289

Z

zero grade, 76, 78, 105, 282-283
Zametkin, Alan, 137

well as teaching classes for gifted and talented students. After leaving teaching, she pursued a number of diverse interests, including professional dog-walking, building aircraft interiors, and corporate training.

In 1993, she joined the staff of Brainworks, where she is kept happily occupied with writing, giving workshops, and assisting clients in the areas of communication and study skills. She also works closely with students and adults on developing coping skills for Attention Deficit Disorder.

About the Authors

Carla Crutsinger received her B.A. from the University of Texas at Austin and earned her M.S. in education from Baylor University. Her teaching experiences cover the elementary, junior high, and high school levels, and she has served on the Texas Advisory Board for Gifted and Talented education. She was the founding president of the Carrollton-Farmers Branch Independent School District Advisory Board for Gifted Children. She has also been listed in Outstanding Young Women of America, Notable Women in Texas, and Who's Who in American Education. Ms. Crutsinger is considered an innovator in education, and her practical workshops have enlightened audiences throughout the country.

A native of Texas, Ms. Crutsinger lives in Carrollton with her husband. They have three sons and two grandsons.

Debra Moore has been fascinated by the English language ever since her father taught her to read when she was three years old. Her interest in words first led her to journalism, but eventually she became an English and history major at East Texas State University, where she earned her B.A. in 1977 and her M.A. in 1980. For thirteen years, she worked as an English instructor for every level from 6th grade to college. Her experience included working with developmental students on basic skills as